Amazon Insects
A Photo Guide

By James L. Castner

GW00503493

Feline P
Gainesville,

Amazon Insects
A Photo Guide

By: James Lee Castner

Published by:
　　　　Feline Press
　　　　P.O. Box 357219
　　　　Gainesville, FL
　　　　32635   USA

© 2000 by Feline Press, Inc.
First Printing 2000
Printed in China
ISBN 0-9625150-1-9

Library of Congress
Catalog Card Number:
99-97053

Table Of Contents

References

Latin American Insects And Entomology. 1993. Charles L. Hogue
University of California Press. Berkeley, CA.

Costa Rican Natural History. 1983. Daniel H. Janzen (Editor)
University of Chicago Press. Chicago, IL.

Butterflies Of South America. 1984. Bernard D'Abrera
Hill House. Victoria, Australia.

Canopy Arthropods. 1997. Nigel E. Stork, J. Adis, R.K. Didham (Editors)
Chapman & Hall. London, England.

Insects Of An Amazon Forest. 1982. Norman D. Penny
Columbia University Press. New York, N.Y.

Introduction

It has always bothered me that there has never been a good photographic identification guide for neotropical insects of the Amazon Basin. Part of the problem is the huge number of species that would have to be treated. Nowhere does the term biodiversity have greater meaning than in the world of insects and arthropods. If current estimates are even close to being correct, there are quite literally millions of insect species in the Amazon rainforest.

To treat thoroughly even one particular insect group could take a lifetime and require volumes. I knew that I could not make a comprehensive reference and did not try. Instead, I chose to present a few dozen of the largest, prettiest, weirdest, and commonest species that I have encountered in my travels throughout the Amazon Basin and in the jungles of South America. I have tried to present this information in a way that is easy to use for biologist and tourist alike. I hope that visitors to tropical forests of the New World will be able to use this simple book to identify some of the invertebrates they see and learn some interesting facts about them. Hopefully this will add to the experience of being in the most marvelous ecological community on Earth.

There was no attempt made to be 'fair' in my coverage of the various insect groups. Certain taxa are only briefly touched, while others are absent completely. Unfortunately, to produce a book that was affordable and appealed to the majority, vast limitations in coverage had to be made.

The physical design and format for *Amazon Insects* was adapted from a work by Patti and Milt Putnam titled *North America's Favorite Butterflies*. Two additional books played a great part in its creation. I have always admired *Costa Rican Natural History* that was edited by Dan Janzen. It provides an abundance of information on all aspects of the tropics, with many individual taxa of the flora and fauna being treated in concise descriptions of two to three pages. The other reference book that stands out as a major work is *Latin American Insects And Entomology* by Charles Hogue. This was of special interest to me because the author spent much of his time in the same geographical area as I have (outside of Iquitos, Peru). Hogue's book probably brings together more information on neotropical entomology than any other. I have tried to combine the best attributes of these books, but in conjunction with color photos of the subjects under discussion. In this way, hopefully all readers will find something that they can enjoy or use from *Amazon Insects*.

I greatly thank Sid Dunkle and Steve Madigosky for the use of their photos, and Jaime Acevedo and Harold Zamorano for reviewing the Spanish. I also thank the many who helped with arthropod identifications including: Christiane Amedegnato, Paul Brock, Carlos Carbonell, Jim Carpenter, Francisco Cerdá, Rex Cocroft, G.B. Edwards, Peter Eliazar, Paul Freytag, Tom Henry, John Heppner, Richard Hoffman, Martin Honey, Gerardo Lamas, Jim Lloyd, Judith Marshall, Jackie and Lee Miller, Dave Nickle, Dan Otte, Lois and Charlie O'Brien, Stewart Peck, Jon Reiskind, Klaus Riede, Julio Rivera, Bob Robbins, Coby Schal, Bill Shear, Sharon Shute, Paul Skelley, Mike Thomas, Mark Whitten, Jim Wiley, Norris Williams, E.O. Wilson, and Bob Woodruff.

Harlequin Beetle   *Acrocinus longimanus*
Length   3 - 4"   **(Coleoptera : Cerambycidae)**

The harlequin beetle belongs to the family of long-horned wood-boring beetles. As the name implies, it has extremely long antennae. This insect is marked with black, yellow, and pink to red coloration all along its top surface in a harlequin-like pattern. The intensity of the colors varies with the individual. Although this pattern appears striking, it blends in well with the lichen-covered tree trunks that the adults frequent. The most striking feature of this species is the long, alien-appearing front legs that are sometimes longer than the body itself.

Acrocinus longimanus

Harlequin beetles lay eggs in dead trees where the larvae feed on the wood, creating galleries as they develop. The life cycle takes about a year to complete. These beetles are able to make squeak-like noises via a stridulatory apparatus. Adults often have pseudoscorpions that live on their body beneath the wing covers where they feed on mites.

El escarabajo arlequín tiene una apariencia extraña con los hermosos colores y las antenas y patas larguísimas. Los inmaduros se desarrollan en la madera de árboles muertos, durando aproximadamente un año.

Giant Ceiba Borer   *Euchroma gigantea*
Length   2.5 - 3"   **(Coleoptera : Buprestidae)**

The giant ceiba borer is one of the most common large beetle species found in tropical forests throughout South and Central America. It is yellow-green in color with an underlying coppery-red tone. It may also be covered with a yellowish powder that looks like pollen, but is actually produced by the adult beetle shortly after it emerges. Females lay their eggs in fallen trees where they hatch and feed on the wood. Trees often used as hosts are ceiba, balsa, and several others. The larvae are called flat-headed borers due to the wide, expanded flattened area behind the head. Adults are commonly seen during the day and are sometimes attracted to oozing saps and resins such as at freshly cut trees. This insect belongs to the family of metallic wood-boring beetles, of which there are more than 3,000 species in the New World. The showy metallic nature of the exoskeleton has resulted in it being used as jewelry. The wing covers have been made into earrings to sell to tourists.

Euchroma gigantea

El catzo o la eucroma es un escarabajo grande y común en la selva amazónica. Se puede encontrar los adultos cerca de los árboles caidos donde las hembras ponen sus huevos. Los inmaduros taladran en el tronco y se comen la madera.

Giant Scarabs ## Subfamily *Dynastinae*

Length 3 - 7" **(Coleoptera : Scarabaeidae)**

In size and strength, there are two beetle groups in South America that are without rival: the Hercules beetles (Genus *Dynastes*) and the rhinoceros beetles (Genus *Megasoma*). Male Hercules beetles have two forward-projecting horns, one above the other, with the top one longest. These are used in fights over females. In *D. hercules* (right) the length of the body and horn together can reach seven inches. Females are without horns and look like typical scarabs. The hard wing covers may be black or yellow-green. Adults feed on tree sap and rotting fruit.

Megasoma elephas

The males of rhinoceros beetles have a large central upturned horn and two smaller thoracic horns. Males of the elephant beetle (*M. elephas*) (left) can get five inches long and weigh 35 grams. These females are also hornless. The grubs mature in dead palm trunks and may also reach five inches in length. Some Amazonian tribes make artifacts from these beetles' horns.

El escarabajo Hércules (derecha) y el escarabajo rinoceronte (arriba) son los más grandes de la cuenca amazónica. Los machos tienen cuernos largos que los usan cuando se pelean. Los adultos comen frutas.

Click Beetles

Length   1 - 3"   **(Coleoptera : Elateridae)**

Pyrophorus sp.

Click beetles are so named because of a mechanism on their underside that allows them to right themselves when placed on their back. This process is usually accompanied by a distinctive click. They all have a long, slender body shape with distinct points at the tips of the pronotum. Color varies greatly (left).

Semiotus sp.

The headlight beetle (Genus *Pyrophorus*) (above left) is one of the most unusual. It has two round light-producing organs located behind the head. There is also a large luminescent organ on the bottom of the first abdominal segment, but it is the dual organs above that give this beetle the aspect of a car with its headlights on. The glow produced is easily seen at a distance and is one of the most curious sights that a visitor can witness.

Semiotus sp.

Los apretadores son escarabajos con cuerpos largos y delgados. El género Pyrophorus (arriba) tiene especies que tienen manchas luminosas.

Fireflies
Length   .5 - 3"   **(Coleoptera : Lampyridae)**

Lucio sp.

A snail-hunting lampyrid.

Lightningbugs or fireflies are neither bugs nor flies, but soft-bodied beetles. They are one of the few insect groups that are truly luminescent. The light-producing organ is on the tip of the adult abdomen and functions in an elaborate system of signals whereby males and females communicate for mating purposes. Most species have noxious chemicals that discourage predators from feeding. At least one species of cockroach is a Batesian mimic of an Amazonian firefly. An unusual member of the firefly family is a 2-3" wingless predator (left) that is encountered on the forest floor where it hunts snails. It has slender, pointed legs and a linear, segmented body. The head can be retracted within a tube and completely hidden and protected. The body has luminescent spots.

Luciérnagas usan luz para comunicarse entre los sexos. Son muy visibles por la noche, pero tienen mal sabor como protección. Un miembro raro de este grupo (izquierda) no tiene alas y es un depredador que caza caracoles en el suelo del bosque.

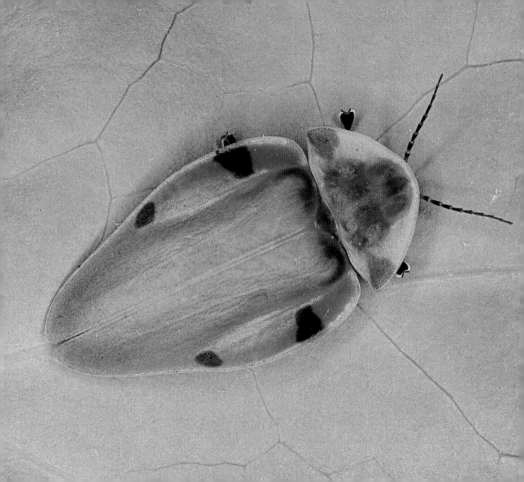

Weevils
Length   .5 - 1.75"   **(Coleoptera : Curculionidae)**

Brentus chiriquensis

Rhyncophorus sp.

Weevils are the biggest family of beetles with more than 12,000 species in the New World and over 50,000 species total. All have elbowed antennae and most have a long, curved snout with tiny mouthparts at the tip. The bodies are squat and robust, or elongate. Bearded weevils are large (2") and have a long tuft of reddish brown hair on the snout that is used in courting. Jeweled weevils have short snouts and dark wing covers with iridescently-colored scales. Brentids or timber weevils (Family Brentidae) (left) vary in size but have a long, narrow body and a long, straight forward-pointing snout. The grubs of the palm weevil (*Rhyncophorus palmarum*) are considered a delicacy in parts of the Amazon.

Los gorgojos comprenden la familia de escarabajos más numerosa, con más de 12,000 especies en Latinoamérica. Normalmente tienen antenas con codos y una naríz muy largo con mandíbulas en el extremo. Algunos como los bréntidos (arriba) son muy delgados.

Tortoise Beetles

Length   .25 - 1"

Subfamily *Cassidinae*

(Coleoptera : Chrysomelidae)

Ischnocodia sp.

Eugenysa sp.

Among the most beautiful of rainforest beetles are the tortoise beetles that look like they have been decorated with liquid gold, although some are pigmented with reds, blues, and greens. Many species are partially transparent. These beetles are rounded or oval in shape, with an extended flat edge. If attacked, they pull their legs and head in (like a tortoise) and hold their shield-like shell pressed tightly to the substrate. Many predators find it impossible to pry them loose. Some species (left) are adorned with a circular 'bull's eye' pattern and are called target tortoise beetles. The immature stages of tortoise beetles are flattened and typically bear many spines. They often occur and feed in groups.

Los escarabajos tortuga son redondos en forma y frecuentemente son dorados (derecha). Muchas especies también son parcialmente transparentes. Cuando amenazados, pueden esconderse bajo la concha.

Pleasing Fungus Beetles
Length   .5 - 1.5"   **(Coleoptera : Erotylidae)**

Homoeotelus d'orbignyi

Cypherotylus sp.

Pleasing or giant fungus beetles are easy to find, as their slow flight and bright colors call attention to themselves. Larger species such as the genus *Erotylus* (right), are strongly convex and have a hump-backed appearance. The black wing covers are often patterned decoratively with wavy lines of yellow, pink, or red. With their shiny luster, the overall effect is of a miniature ambulatory glazed ceramic piece. The larvae of pleasing fungus beetles feed on various types of fungi. Large groups can sometimes be found in the undersides of bracket fungi that blanket fallen trees. The festive pigments adorning the adults are evidently warning coloration, as the beetles can exude a noxious liquid from the legs and anus.

Los escarabajos gigantes hongo se mueven y vuelan lentemente. Tienen una joroba y frecuentemente líneas de colores brillantes en un fondo de negro (derecha). Pueden producir una sustancia nociva como defensa.

Morpho Butterflies   Genus *Morpho*
Wingspan   3 - 6"   **(Lepidoptera : Morphidae)**

Few sights elicit as much excitement from the first-time visitor to a rainforest as that of a morpho butterfly on the wing. Some species have nearly a six-inch wingspan and their electric blue color makes them unforgettable. The genus *Morpho* has over 80 species distributed throughout Central and South America with greatest diversity in the Amazon Basin. The cobalt blue color is not due to pigments, but rather the refraction and reflection of light caused by the unique structure of the wing scales. Males are more colorful than females, although both sexes are a dull brown with small eyespots on the undersurface.

Morpho sp.

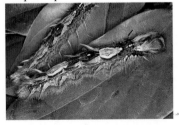

Some species are nearly totally white. The larvae of morphos (left) are very hairy and often colorful, sometimes feeding in large aggregations. Host plants occur in several families, including the legumes and grasses. The adults feed on rotting fruit and tree sap. Males are attracted to other males and can be lured in by blue decoys. Several species are currently being raised commercially.

Los morfos son mariposas grandes, bien conocidas por su color azul brillante. La parte abajo de las alas es café y críptica. Los adultos comen frutas podridas y las resinas de árboles. Las orugas son muy peludas.

Owl Butterflies   Genus *Caligo*
Wingspan   3 - 6"   (Lepidoptera : Brassolidae)

Owl butterflies in the genus *Caligo* (right) are among the largest of rainforest butterflies. They are so named due to the large eyespot on each of the hind wings which are used to thwart off or misdirect attacks. They are active in the forest understory at dawn and dusk, but are sometimes startled into flight from their daytime resting sites which are usually on the trunks of trees. The adults feed on rotting fruit, tree sap, carrion, and dung.

Caligo sp.

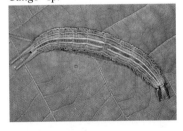

The large larva (left) is distinctive with a forked tail and a spiny margin around the head capsule. It may look like a slender brown slug in the later stages. Owl butterfly caterpillars feed on the leaves of banana and heliconia plants, and certain palms. The chrysalis is a beautiful smooth, mottled brown structure with two gold spots. It resembles a dead curled leaf with tiny 'windows' of light shining through.

La mariposa búho crepuscular come frutas podridas cuando es adulta y las hojas de banana y palmas cuando es oruga. Tiene un 'ojo' en cada ala trasera. Estos ojos falsos sirven para intimidar a los enemigos y dirigir ataques fuera del cuerpo.

Blush Butterflies **Genus *Cithaerias***
Wingspan   1.5 - 3"   **(Lepidoptera : Satyridae)**

The genus *Cithaerias* has less than a dozen species, most of which occur in the Amazon. Most members of this group have nearly completely transparent wings with the venation clearly visible. They have received their unofficial common name due to the 'blush' of color that occurs on the hind wings. This may be a hot pink, blue, or sometimes even yellow. There is also a small single eyespot on the hind wing which separates it from a similar genus (*Haetera*) that has two eyespots. Little is known of the larvae or their foodplants.

The blush butterflies exhibit a very distinctive and characteristic flight behavior. They fly very low to the forest floor, often no more than 6-12 inches above the leaf litter. In the ground level darkness, one often sees only a flitting glimpse of these transparent butterflies near small light gaps. They are very difficult to approach closely, tending to alight at a distance of 6-10 feet away, where they will sit motionless on foliage. However, when their individual space is violated, they will take off for a short distance then once again settle on a leaf or foliage. Painstaking stalking (or luck) is needed to approach these species.

'Las mariposas rubor' son especies con alas casi totalmente transparentes, con la excepción de una mancha grande de color rosado, azul, o amarillo en las alas traseras. Vuelan muy cerca a la tierra y es difícil acercárseles.

Swallowtail Butterflies   *Parides* and *Eurytides*
Wingspan   2 - 4"   **(Lepidoptera : Papilionidae)**

Parides sp. © S. Madigosky

Twig-like chrysalis

This butterfly family gets its name from a long slender extension of the hind wing found on many species. The genus *Eurytides* has about fifty species, many with extremely long 'tails' that has led to the name swordtails. Large numbers of mixed species of these butterflies are often seen drinking liquids from mud or along river banks (right). The genus *Parides* is varied in appearance, but generally has dark-winged adults with large spots or bands of color or transparency on each of the wings. Some species have 'tails', while others do not. Larvae often resemble bird droppings and are brown or mottled. They can evert a structure from behind the head and release a pungent odor if disturbed. The chrysalids are superb imitations of twigs.

Las mariposas con cola de golondrina compren-den varias especies que se encuentran con frecuencia cerca del barro y de las orillas (derecha). Las orugas se parecen a las heces de aves y los crisálidos a ramitas.

Metalmark Butterflies

Wingspan   .5 - 2.5"   (Lepidoptera : Riodinidae)

The riodinids or metalmarks comprise a large family with more than 2,000 species whose greatest diversity is found in the Amazon region. This group has no set 'look' or 'gestalt' to it, but has members that resemble many other butterfly and moth families. The genus *Helicopis* (right) for example, has species with long 'tails' on the hind wings that are reminiscent of hairstreak or lycaenid butterflies. Others (left) have colors that are startling in their bril-

Rhetus   arcius

liance. The riodinids are among the most vividly pigmented of all the neotropical butterflies. Riodinids occur from southern Mexico to southern Brazil. Some adults exhibit the unusual behavior of hiding flattened out beneath a leaf, with just the eyes and antennae peeking out and visible. Although little is known about the larvae, they have been recorded from a wide variety of foodplants. Some riodinid caterpillars have symbiotic relationships with ants which guard them and in return feed on an exudate the larvae make.

Estas mariposas costituyen una familia con muchos colores y mucha variedad. Algunas tienen colores brillantes (arriba) mientras otras tienen 'colitas' largas (derecha). Unas de las orugas viven bajo la protección de las hormigas.

Passion Vine Butterflies
Wingspan   2 - 4"   **(Lepidoptera : Heliconidae)**

Heliconius ismenius

Philaethria dido

Dryas julia

This is a group of about 70 large, brightly colored species that are all found in the New World. Also known as heliconian butterflies, they have large eyes, long clubbed antennae, and long slender oval fore wings that range from 3-4". As larvae, they feed almost exclusively on passion vines (Family Passifloraceae). The genus *Heliconius* has spiny larvae. The adults of many are foul-tasting and advertise the fact with bright colors and a slow, almost 'lazy' type of gliding flight. Species of *Heliconius* have evolved the ability to feed on pollen. Regular visits to flowering plants in the genera *Psiguria* and *Gurania* (Family Cucurbitaceae) provide the adults with a near constant nutrient source, which has led to un-usually long life spans. The pupae tend to be sculptured and may have metallic spots.

Las mariposas del sol tienen orugas espinosas que comen las hojas de granadillas. Los adultos del género Heliconius tienen colores brillantes y son los únicos que comen polen.

Clearwing Butterflies

Wingspan   2 - 3"   **(Lepidoptera : Ithomiidae)**

Oleria sp.

Mechanitis isthmia

The ithomiine or clearwing butterflies comprise
several hundred neotropical species. Many
species have nearly totally transparent wings
(right). Others are brown, black, and yellow,
colors shared by many heliconian butterflies.
Wing shape is slender and oval, making the
ithomiines and heliconians difficult to tell apart.
Male clearwings however, have patches of long
hairs (androconia) on the hind wings where the
fore wings overlap. The larvae of glasswings are
smooth and feed on nightshades (Family Solanaceae). The noxious chemicals in the foodplants
are passed on to the adults of many species which
show warning colors and belong to Müllerian
mimicry rings with the heliconians and others.
The pupae of some species are curved and look
like reflective droplets of molten silver or gold.

*Las mariposas con alas de vidrio son muy
parecidas a las mariposas del sol. Las orugas
comen plantas de la familia Solanaceae.*

White and Sulfur Butterflies

Wingspan   1 - 3"   **(Lepidoptera : Pieridae)**

Perrhybris pamela

Dismorphia amphione

The pierid butterflies are frequently seen from boats as they 'puddle' along tropical river banks. They often congregate in great numbers at a muddy spot or where a large animal has recently urinated. By probing the damp soil or sand with their tongues, they obtain valuable minerals and nutrients. When disturbed, they erupt in a swirling cloud of white, yellow, and orange. Most species are small or medium-sized butterflies with rounded wings . The genus *Dismorphia* is atypical in having species with slender elongate wings that are brightly colored or sometimes transparent. These species are evidently Batesian mimics of the heliconian and ithomiine butterflies which they resemble greatly. Many species of pierids are migratory, and some are pests.

La mayoría de estas mariposas son blancas o amarillas, sin embargo algunas parecen especies de las familias Ithomiidae y Heliconidae. Grupos grandes son atraidos al fango y a la arena mojada con orina donde chupan los nutrientes.

Swallowtail Moths   Genus *Urania*

Wingspan   3 - 4"   **(Lepidoptera : Uranidae)**

The swallowtail or birdwing moth, sometimes called the green urania, is unusual in being a daytime flyer. Its rapid, agile flight is difficult to miss as these moths are often attracted to sweat on clothing or can be seen 'puddling' at mud or in damp sand. The moth itself is unmistakable with long, light-colored tails the shape and size of a swallowtail butterfly's and beautiful bands of iridescent green to coppery pigments on black wings. The colors are so dazzling as to appear fake or painted on at first glance.

There are four species of *Urania*, with *Urania leilus* found in the Amazon Basin. The distribution of the moth evidently follows the range of its euphorbiaceous larval foodplants, which are lianas in the genus *Omphalea*. Both *Urania leilus* and *Urania fulgens* of Central America are known to undergo massive seasonal migrations every few years. The reason for this is unknown, but it may act as a dispersal mechanism.

La polilla con cola de golondrina es insólita porque vuela durante el día. Se encuentran con frecuencia cerca del barro o de la arena mojada. Los colores de los adultos son tan brillantes que parecen artificiales. Hay épocas cuando grandes cantidades de estas polillas migran a nuevas tierras. Hay cuatro especies, que también se llaman la urania verde. Las orugas comen las hojas de lianas en el género Omphalea.

Wasp Moths
Wingspan   1 - 2"

(Lepidoptera : Arctiidae)

Macrocneme sp.

Hyalurga fenestra

The wasp moths include species from several sub-families, but especially the Ctenuchinae. They are generally diurnal mimetic moths that resemble wasps, bees, and beetles. In some species (right) the wings may be nearly transparent. Others such as some of the tiger moths may be totally dark and have metallic or iridescent pigments. Some mimic the banded pattern of adult net-winged beetles. The weedy plant heliotrope (genus *Heliotropium*) is very attractive to some of these adult moths, which are sometimes found on them in large numbers. It is theorized that the plant contains useful chemicals, such as those used by clearwing butterflies as precursors to their sex pheromones. The flight of many wasp moths exactly matches that of their stinging models.

Las polillas avispa imitan a las avispas en apariencia y comportamiento. Son diurnas y se parecen a escarabajos, abejas, y avispas. Algunas especies tienen alas transparentes (derecha) mientras otras tienen colores brillantes.

Peacock Moths

Wingspan   2 - 4"   **(Lepidoptera : Saturniidae)**

These moths are so named for their habit of suddenly flashing open their hind wings, much in the way a male peacock fans out its tail feathers. Also called eyed saturnians, the above action results in two large colorful eyespots being displayed (below). Such a startle display is sometimes enough to intimidate an attacker, allowing the moth to escape harm. When at rest (right), the dull-colored fore wings completely cover the hind wings and provide a cryptic and camouflaged appearance. The adult moths are often attracted to lights.

Automeris sp.

The larvae of many species of peacock moths are covered with urticating spines. The colors of the caterpillars vary greatly, but usually tend to be bright and easily recognizable. There are nearly 200 species of peacock moths, only a small portion of which inhabit the Amazon lowlands. The io moth of North America belongs to the common tropical genus *Automeris*.

Las polillas pavo real tienen manchas en las alas traseras que parecen ojos. Normalmente, estas manchas son escondidas, sin embargo, cuando algo le molesta a la nocturna, abre las alas para revelar 'los ojos grandes'. Esta amenaza a los depredadores que a menudo paran el ataque.

48

Rothschildia Moths
Wingspan   4 - 6"

Genus *Rothschildia*
(Lepidoptera : Saturniidae)

These are large, beautiful moths with triangular or oval transparent areas in both the fore wings and the hind wings. These 'windows' have led to the common name window-winged saturnian (the last word deriving from the family name). Over twenty species of these moths have been described from Central and South America, more than half with ranges in the Andes. Most species are pigmented with various shades of brown, sometimes almost ochre. However, specimens nearly orange in color have also been observed. Different color morphs of the same species can result from changing environmental

Rothschildia sp.

conditions (wet vs. dry). In shape and size, the window-winged saturnians appear most similar to the cynthia or ailanthus silk moth that is now established in North America. Mature larvae (left) get up to three inches in length and are brightly colored with alternating bands of green, black, and orange. They have small harmless spines and feed on a variety of foodplants including crops.

Las polillas de cuatro ventanas (derecha) tienen más de veinte especies en el Nuevo Mundo. Tienen los colores del café, pero algunos especímenes son casi anaranjados. La oruga (arriba) tiene anillos de color verde, negro, y naranja. Comen muchas plantas, incluyendo algunos cultivos.

White Witch   *Thysania agrippina*
Wingspan   8 - 12"   **(Lepidoptera : Noctuidae)**

The white witch, also called the birdwing moth, is one of the rainforest giants.
This huge insect has one of the greatest wingspans of any moth in the world. It
has a white to gray base color with dark striations in a wavy pattern throughout
the wings. The front wings are considerably longer than the hind wings, both
of which are scalloped along the edges. The white witch might at first be
confused with one of the giant silk moths (Family Saturniidae), but it has fine,
thread-like antennae rather than the plumose or feathery antennae of saturniids.

One might think a moth this large would find it difficult to go unnoticed in a
tropical forest full of predators. However, the color and patterns found on the
birdwing moth's wings can perfectly match the striated, lichen-covered bark
found on so many rainforest trees. As long as the moth orients itself correctly
with the markings in a vertical direction to match the tree (right), the camouflage is extremely effective.

---

*La bruja blanca o emperador es una de las mariposas nocturnas más grandes
del mundo. Tiene un color de base gris con líneas oscuras y curvas en las
alas. Estas líneas son muy parecidas a las líneas de la corteza en troncos,
cuyo color sirve para esconder la polilla cuando está en el lado de un árbol
que esté cubierto con líquenes (derecha).*

Sphinx Moths

Wingspan   2 - 6"   **(Lepidoptera : Sphingidae)**

The sphingids or hawk moths are easy to recognize with their thick torpedo-like bodies and triangular fore wings that are much larger than the hind wings. Sphinx moths have the streamlined appearance of a jet fighter when at rest. The reference to a sphinx comes from the classic pose the larvae adopt when disturbed. Caterpillars are also called hornworms, as many possess a horn or flexible spine at the end of the abdomen. A large tropical hornworm commonly seen is *Pseudosphinx tetrio* (below). These caterpillars have warning coloration and will use their heads to butt attackers. Large numbers can completely defoliate their food tree of frangipani.

Pseudosphinx tetrio

Sphinx moths hover like hummingbirds when feeding on nectar from flowers. They have extremely long tongues and are solely responsible for pollinating certain tropical species of plants, most of which have flowers with long tubular bases. Many species are camouflaged at rest (right).

Este grupo tiene polillas con cuerpos gruesos y gusanos cornudos. Los adultos tienen lenguas larguísimas y vuelan como picaflores cuando están chupando el néctar de las flores. La mayoría de estas polillas son camufladas, pero algunas orugas tienen colores de aviso como la especie arriba.

Dragonflies

Wingspan   2 - 5"

Suborder *Anisoptera*

(Order : Odonata)

Orthemis schmidti   (male)

Dragonflies are common diurnal insects most often seen near ponds, lakes, and streams. They are extremely agile and rapid flyers with large, bulging compound eyes. Their membranous wings are always held out at right angles from the body. The wings may be clear, dark, or banded; while the body may be dull or vividly-colored, depending on the species. The immature stages of dragonflies are aquatic and predatory. The adults feed on small insects that they catch on the wing. Adults are territorial in nature and often engage in aerial 'dogfights'. There are more than a thousand neotropical species, most belonging to the group of common skimmers (Family Libellulidae). (All photos on pages 54-59 are the copyrighted property of Dr. Sidney W. Dunkle)

Zenithoptera americana (m.)

Uracis fastigiata   (male)

Los chinchilejos o libélulas son los voladores más poderosos del mundo de los insectos. Las alas pueden ser transparentes, oscuras, o con manchas. Son depredadores como adultos y también en las etapas inmaduras.

Damselflies   Suborder *Zygoptera*

Wingspan   1 - 4"   **(Order : Odonata)**

Damselflies are very similar to dragonflies, but are capable of folding the wings back over the abdomen when at rest. Their bodies are also more slender and delicate in appearance, and they are weaker flyers. The wings are usually transparent, although the bodies may be beautifully pigmented. There are more than a thousand species of damselflies in the New World tropics. Damselflies pass their immature stages in the water, preying upon small aquatic organisms. The adults usually remain near the area where they developed. Their diet

Argia sp. (male)

© S. Dunkle

consists of tiny insects which are scooped up while flying with legs that are covered with slender spines. Broad-winged damselflies (Family Calopterygidae) and narrow-winged damselflies (Family Coenagri-onidae) (left & right) are common through-out Amazonia. The spread-winged damsel-flies (Family Lestidae) rest with their wings partially spread out or opened.

Estes chinchilejos tienen cuerpos delgados y alas transparentes. Hay más de mil especies en las áreas tropicales del Nuevo Mundo. Los inmaduros viven en el agua donde comen pequeños organismos acuáticos.

Microstigma rotundatum (female)
© S. Dunkle

Giant Damselflies

Suborder *Zygoptera*

Wingspan 4 - 8"

(Odonata : Pseudostigmatidae)

Mecistogaster lucretia (male)

© S. Dunkle

These large, delicate-appearing insects are also known as helicopter damselflies due to the way in which the wings slowly beat. They are found throughout the Amazon Basin and extend into northern Mexico. The largest species has a wingspan of almost eight inches and a body length of four. Females place their eggs in treeholes or bromeliads, where they develop. Adults are specialized predators on spiders, taking them both from foliage and directly out of webs. Target species are small orb weavers and the kleptoparasitic spiders in the webs of large orb weavers. The genus *Megaloprepus* has a single species (*M. coerulatus*) with purple bands of color on transparent wings. The genus *Mecistogaster* (left) is also found in the Amazon region, but has red, yellow, or orange coloration near the wing tips. Some males are territorial and will defend a selected area of forest against other males.

Los helicópteros son los chinchilejos más grandes del mundo. Sus alas se mueven muy lentamente. Capturan y comen arañas de hojas y de telas. Las hembras ponen los huevos en bromelias donde se desarollan.

Sylvan Katydids
Length   1 - 4"

Subfamily *Pseudophyllinae*
(Orthoptera : Tettigoniidae)

Championica sp.

Leptotettix voluptarius

Acanthodis sp.

The sylvan katydids are a diverse group in size, color, body shape, and behavior. Also called the pseudophyllines, this subfamily name literally means 'false leaf' and is appropriate as the true leaf-mimicking katydids are contained within this group. Others include the largest and heaviest Amazonian katydid, bark/twig/moss-mimicking species, dark spindle-shaped species, and even a member with a rare bright pink color form (right).

Roosting behavior in this group has revealed species specific traits. Cryptic species tend to remain visible and are protected by their camouflage, while non-camouflaged species often pass the day inside dead leaves or out of sight in other refuges. Some individuals use the same roost day after day and will defend it against intruders.

Los grillos del bosque son un grupo muy diverso en tamaño, color, forma y comportamiento. Hay miembros con camuflaje de hojas, corteza, musgo y ramitas. Otros se esconden en hojas muertas.

Spiny Lobster
Length   3.5 - 4.5"

Panoploscelis specularis
(Orthoptera : Tettigoniidae)

This is the biggest and heaviest katydid in the Upper Amazon. Females may reach a length of nearly five inches and weigh up to 3-4 ounces when gravid. The egg-laying device (ovipositor) is a large, broad, flat structure that sticks straight out from the female's abdomen like a sword. The body is dark brown and cigar-shaped with six large powerful legs that are all covered with spines. Unlike most katydids, this species has very short wings (brachypterous) that lie almost flat over the thorax. A special 'file' and 'scraper' (one on one wing and one on the other) enable the spiny lobster to make sounds. Its call is a double

Panoploscelis specularis

click, one repeated right after the other. The female can call as well as the male in this species, another unusual feature in the katydid world. Although fearsome in appearance, these katydids are gentle giants and can be handled with little danger. Their normal diet includes the leaves of banana and heliconia plants, although they are probably opportunistic on other things.

La langosta espinosa (arriba y derecha) es el grillo más grande y más pesado en la cuenca amazónica. Tiene alas cortas y patas poderosas que están cubiertas con espinas. El cuerpo es de color café y tiene la forma de un cigarro.

Leaf Katydids
Length   .75 - 4"

Tribe *Pterochrozini*
(Orthoptera : Tettigoniidae)

Roxelana crassicornis

Typophyllum trigonum

Among the sylvan katydids is the group known as the true leaf mimics. These are katydids whose resemblance to leaves is exact in every detail. Their wings are often irregularly shaped and bear markings that appear to be holes, fungi, and feeding damage. In one species, there are even brown and white markings that appear to be a bird dropping. Immature leaf katydids have wing pads that develop straight up from the back, giving them the appearance of miniature stego-saurs in the later nymphal stages. There are approximately 100 described species of true leaf-mimicking katydids in 13 genera distributed throughout Central and South America.

Grillos hoja son insectos que se parecen exactamente a las hojas. Algunas especies (derecha) tienen alas con huecos falsos y manchas que imitan hongos. Hay una especie que tiene en las alas los colores de las heces fecales de un ave.

Leaf Katydids
Length   .75 - 4"

Tribe *Pterochrozini*
(Orthoptera : Tettigoniidae)

Typophyllum lunatum

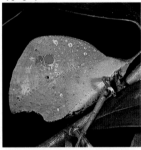

Typophyllum sp.

In the Upper Amazon, leaf mimics are represented primarily by the genera: *Pterochroza*, *Cycloptera*, *Roxelana*, and *Typophyllum*. The species of *Pterochroza* are large, rectangular-winged insects with a startle display that has resulted in them being called peacock katydids. The species of *Cycloptera* are drip-tip katydids, with green adults whose wings end in a pronounced point. *Roxelana crassicornis* is light green with rounded wings and the single species in its genus. It has been dubbed the 'green screamer' due to its constant calling during night or day. The genus *Typophyllum* is extremely diverse with several dozen species, many of which exhibit color variants and sexual dimorphism.

El género Typophyllum (izquierda y derecha) es lo más diverso con más de 35 especies. Normalmente la hembra es más grande que el macho. Algunas veces los dos sexos tienen formas y colores diferentes.

Bolivar's Katydid
Length   1 - 3"

Typophyllum bolivari
(Orthoptera : Tettigoniidae)

Typophyllum bolivari (male)

Typophyllum bolivari (male)

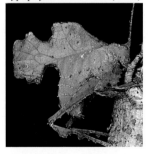

The male and female of this species are markedly different in size and shape. The adult male (left) is about an inch in length and has squarish wings that have a large notch in the upper and lower edges. The adult female (right) gets up to three inches in length and has much longer wings that taper to a point. Both sexes may be either light brown, green, or mottled brown. The colors become fixed during development and can not change chameleon-like. The antennae of both sexes have distinctive knobs at intervals along the entire length. The hind legs are flattened and scalloped. There are dark striations on the membranous hind wings that may be displayed briefly if the insect is disturbed.

El grillo de Bolivar existe en muchos colores incluyendo crema, verde, y en una fase manchada con pardo. El macho (arriba) es pequeño (1") y parece faltarle porciones de las alas. La hembra (derecha) es grande (3") y tiene alas puntiagudas.

Peacock Katydids

Length   3 - 4"

Genus *Pterochroza*

(Orthoptera : Tettigoniidae)

Pterochroza uniexcisa

Pterochroza sp.

Pterochroza ocellata

The peacock katydids all resemble dead or diseased leaves at rest. They are named for their impressive intimidation display. When disturbed, they flick up their front wings to reveal the colors and eyespots (right) on the hind wings in hopes of scaring away the intruder. When viewed from behind while displaying, the katydid resembles an avian face. After a minute or so, the wings close and the colors disappear, often as the katydid hops into the leaf litter. Both the male and the female peacock katydids display. They are the largest of the neotropical true leaf-mimicking katydids and exhibit many different colors and patterns. All however have wide wings that are roughly rectangular in shape. The late immatures are unique with upright wingpads that stick straight out from the back and criss-cross.

Los grillos pavo real toman su nombre de su exhibición (derecha) de intimidación. Con las alas cerradas, parecen hojas muertas (izquierda).

Conehead Katydids

Subfamily *Copiphorinae*

Length   1.5 - 4"

(Orthoptera : Tettigoniidae)

Bucrates sp.

Loboscelis sp.

Dadaelellus sp.

The conehead katydids are easily recognized by a large horn in the middle of the top of their head. While large and easily visible in most species, others have it reduced to a small spike between the bases of the antennae. The copiphorine katydids also have dark pigmentation around the mandibles. There are numerous neotropical species, most with full-sized wings as adults. An exception is the common genus *Dadaelellus* (left), which has small abbreviated wings. Female coneheads tend to have a long ovipositor (egg-laying structure) that sticks straight back from the abdomen like a sword. Coneheads have been observed feeding on the fruits of aroid plants. Adults are known to communicate via tremulations or vibrations that are carried along the plant or substrate upon which they are resting.

Los grillos con cabeza cornuda tienen una espina en el centro de la cabeza y mandíbulas fuertes y con colores. Las hembras tienen 'espadas' largas y las usan para poner sus huevos.

Spiny Devil Katydid
Length   2.5 - 3"

Panacanthus cuspidatus
(Orthoptera : Tettigoniidae)

This katydid belongs to the subfamily of coneheads (Copiphorinae), which are characterized by a spike arising from the top of the head. In this species, there is a huge, three-pointed red horn that sticks straight up. There are also large

Panacanthus   cuspidatus

green spines around the head and flat face reaching from the large yellow eyes to the mouthparts (right). The legs are green with yellow tips, but all are covered with multiple rows of spines (left).

The spiny devil has a distinctive threatening posture when provoked. It holds its front legs out wide while opening its large and extremely powerful jaws. The mandibles are tipped with black and the display results in a very formidable appearance. Large internal muscles supply the power to its jaws which normally work on forest seeds and fruits. While most katydids are unable to break the skin of humans, this particular species is an exception.

El grillo diablo espinoso tiene una corona de espinas verdes alrededor de la cara y un gran cuerno rojo y puntiagudo en el centro. Las patas también están cubiertas con filas de espinas. Tiene una exhibición feroz con las mandíbulas abiertas.

Rainbow Katydids   Genus *Vestria*
Length 3"   **(Orthoptera : Tettigoniidae)**

This genus includes the orange rainbow katydid (below) and the true rainbow katydid (right). On the latter species the legs are yellow, green, blue, and white with orange 'feet' or tarsi. The abdomen has alternating rings of blue and yellow, while the wings are a transparent green and the head a pale orange. The orange rainbow katydid has transparent wings and a pale orange head and body, the latter decorated with purple and black spots. The legs vary from pink to maroon with reddish-orange tarsi.

Vestria sp.

When disturbed, rainbow katydids move their wings upward and forward while curling the abdomen, exposing the bright colors. A small gland at the tip of the body also releases a warning odor that is very distinctive. The combination of colors and odor theoretically warn visually-orienting diurnal predators and non-visually orienting nocturnal predators that these insects are bad tasting. Field experiments bear this out.

Los grillos arcoiris tienen colores brillantes que avisan a los depredadores que tienen mal sabor. Cuando son molestados, levantan las alas para mostrar claramente los colores de aviso y también sueltan un olor distintivo.

Bush Katydids

Length   .75 - 4"

Subfamily *Phaneropterinae*
(Orthoptera : Tettigoniidae)

Hyperphrona sp.

Euceraia sp.

Steirodon sp.

The bush katydids are composed of many species that are primarily green and have rounded-oval or straight slender wings. They are often attracted to lights and are among the most easily seen of nocturnal katydids. Some species have brightly colored abdomens (genus *Itarissa*), while others like the collared katydids (genus *Euceraia*)(left) have the area directly behind the head brightly pigmented. A few species are spectacularly camouflaged such as the rotting leaf mimics (genus *Pycnopalpa*)(right). Others are among the most convincing of wasp mimics (genus *Aganacris*). The largest phaneropterines are the saddleback katydids (genus *Steirodon*)(left), which have a large saddle-like area immediately behind the head. Large specimens may approach four inches in length.

La mayoría de los grillos arbusto son verdes y tienen alas redondas-ovaladas o delgadas. De noche, son atraídos por las luces. Los más grandes pertenecen al género Steirodon.

Wasp Katydids   Genus *Aganacris*
Length   2 - 3"   (Orthoptera : Tettigoniidae)

The genus *Aganacris* has several species that mimic wasps in both appearance and behavior. In the Upper Amazon region, the males of *A. pseudosphex* can sometimes be collected at lights at night. It is a classic example of Batesian mimicry where spider wasps (Family Pompilidae) are the most probable models. This species is sexually dimorphic with the male (right) having a black body with white markings and nearly transparent yellow-tinted wings. The female (below) has a metallic blue-black body with some white markings and opaque blue-tinted wings. In both sexes the antennae are severely short-

Aganacris pseudosphex (female)

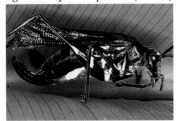

ened, and moved in a rapid, almost nervous manner similar to that of hunting wasps. The tip of the abdomen is also moved up and down in a characteristic stinging motion. In Brazil, other wasp-mimicking katydids with similar anatomical and behavioral features are found in the genus *Scaphura*.

Esta especie de grillo parece una avispa e imita el comportamiento de una avispa. El macho (derecha) tiene alas transparentes con un poquito de amarillo. La hembra (arriba) tiene alas oscuras con un color azul-negro.

Predaceous Katydids

Length   .5 - 2"

Subfamily *Listroscelidinae*
(Orthoptera : Tettigoniidae)

Phlugis sp.

Phlugis sp.

Phlugiola redtenbacheri

Most katydids are herbivores, but the listroscelidines are genera whose species are carnivorous. *Phlugiola* and *Phlugis* (left) contain small individuals with large eyes that are diurnal predators. Their front legs are covered with large spines used to capture gnats and other tiny arthropods. These species are often seen on the top surface of leaves awaiting their prey, however they can rapidly dart to the underside to escape danger.

The impaler katydid (*Monocerophora* sp.)(right) is the largest Amazonian listroscelidine. It is nearly two inches in length and has huge spikes that line the front legs in double rows. It is also unusual in having a 'long' face with distinctive white accessory appendages (palpi). Its slender brown and green body is unmistakable.

Hay géneros de pequeños grillos depredadores cuyas especies tienen ojos grandes y cazan diurna. Otra como 'el empalero' (derecha) es más grande y tiene espinas en las patas.

Acridid Short-Horned Grasshoppers

Length   1 - 5"   **(Orthoptera : Acrididae)**

Mastusia quadricarinata

Ommatolampis perpiscillata

Syntomacris sp.

These are common diurnal insects that exhibit a tremendous variety of forms and colors through out the Amazon Basin. They typically have short antennae which are usually less than the length of the body, and an enlarged hind leg for jumping. The eggs of many species are laid in the soil and covered with a protective secretion. Grasshoppers exploit almost all habitats, including aquatic ones. They are found from the forest floor to the peak of the canopy. The family Acrididae contains many subfamilies, some of which are considered families themselves, depending upon the taxonomist. Acridids from the Upper Amazon are very diverse in size, shape, and color. Most have wings, but some are wingless or have tiny wing remnants (left center) and are flightless.

Los saltamontes tienen antenas cortas y patas grandes traseras que usan para saltar. Tienen muchas formas y colores, y viven en una variedad de lugares incluyendo los acuáticos.

Romaleid Short-Horned Grasshoppers
Length   1 - 5"   **(Orthoptera : Romaleidae)**

Prionacris cantrix

The romaleids are a diverse family of grasshoppers containing more than 200 species. The majority of these are found in the tropical regions of South and Central America. This family includes the lubbers, which are large brightly colored, foul-tasting species that often have threatening displays. When young, lubbers tend to group together on plants. The birdwing grasshoppers (*Tropidacris* spp.) are also included in this family. They are the largest grasshoppers and may have a wingspan of 10", with blue or red hind wings. The romaleid fauna of the Amazon region includes leaf mimics (left center), short-winged canopy species (left bottom), and many species of more typical grasshopper appearance. Many romaleids are large, robust insects with a granulate texture to the integument surface.

Colpolopha latipennis

Hyleacris rubrogranulata

Los saltamontes romaléidos incluyen formas que parecen hojas (izquierda centro), formas de la colpa con alas cortas (izquierda abajo), y formas generales. La mayoría son grandes insectos.

Pygmy and Pyrgomorph Grasshoppers

Length   1 - 5"   **(Orthoptera : Tetrigidae / Pyrgomorphidae)**

Scaria sp.

Omura congrua

Omura congrua

The pygmy grasshoppers (Family Tetrigidae) have more than a thousand species worldwide. Also called tetrigids, they are easy to identify because the normally collar-like structure (pronotum) behind the head extends all the way back over the abdomen. Although generally cryptic, some like the genus *Scaria* (left top) have bright, iridescent colors. In some species, the pronotum is greatly extended in a manner similar to some treehoppers. These species usually resemble leaves, twigs, or pebbles.

Pyrgomorphs are easily recognized by their narrow, conical head with antennae often held straight up and out. *Omura congrua* is wingless and flattened, and one of the most widespread pyrgomorph grasshoppers in the Amazon Basin.

Los saltamontes pigmeo o tetrígidos tienen un prontoum que extiende al extremo del abdomen (izquierda arriba y derecha). Los saltamontes pyrgomorfo tienen cabezas cónicas como la especie común Omura congrua (izquierda).

Airplane Grasshoppers
Length   1"
(Orthoptera : Eumastacidae)

Pseudomastax personata

Pseudomastax sp.

The eumastacids, also called airplane or monkey grasshoppers, are one of the easiest groups to identify due to their characteristic posture. Both the adults and the immatures hold the hind legs from the body at right angles. This gives them the appearance of miniature airplanes. They are also unusual in having extremely narrow wings which are held vertically above the body, leaving almost the entire abdomen exposed. The hind tibiae on eumastacids have a row of large spines that are used for defense. Airplane grasshoppers are often found perched on the foliage of the weedy growth that springs up in disturbed areas, or that borders forests. Some species are dull-colored with light spots or stripes, while others have intense greens, blues, and yellows.

Los saltamontes avioneta tienen una postura muy distintiva. Mantienen las patas traseras en un ángulo de noventa grados al cuerpo. Algunos tienen colores brillantes y otros colores oscuros.

Jumping Sticks
Length   2.5 - 5"   **(Orthoptera : Proscopiidae)**

The proscopiid grasshoppers are large insects and form a common component of the Amazonian insect fauna. They are also known as jumping sticks and are sometimes irreverantly referred to as 'Nixon grasshoppers', due to the large

Apioscelis   bulbosa

'jowls' on the faces of some species such as *Apioscelis* (left). The wings are either absent or very small and non-functional. The antennae are very short and stubby. Although the legs tend to be slender, the hind femora are slightly enlarged as found in most grass-hoppers. Proscopiids are capable of jumping, but only weakly. They are obvious when on foliage but well-concealed when on twigs or branches. The male is about half the size of the female and is often found riding on top of her (right). Most species are dull-colored, but some have yellow and red pigmentation. Although easily mistaken for walkingsticks, the latter have long antennae. Jumping sticks are found only in South America ranging no farther north than Panama.

Los saltamontes proscópidos son grandes y parecen palitos. No tienen alas, o en algunos casos, tienen alas muy pequeñas. Pueden saltar, pero sólo débilmente. Existen con frecuencia en pares copulando (derecha).

Mole Crickets

Length   1 - 3"

Scapteriscus **and** *Neocurtilla*

(Orthoptera : Gryllotalpidae)

Mole crickets are burrowing insects that are cylindrical in shape and have large claws on the front legs that they use for digging. Species with two claws belong to the genus *Scapteriscus* (right), while species with four claws may belong to several genera, including *Neocurtilla* (below). The largest neotropical species, *Scapteriscus oxydactylus*, is often found on ephemeral islands along the Amazon and Napo Rivers as the water levels drop.

Neocurtilla sp.

Some mole crickets feed on roots and young plants while others consume tiny soil arthropods. Their passage through the sand or soil surface leaves traces that look like miniature mole hills. Most species have full-sized wings and are capable of flying. Three species of *Scapteriscus* have been accidentally introduced into the United States where they are pests of turf and agriculture. Mole crickets are often seen on the ground at night under lights.

Los grillotalpos tienen uñas grandes en las patas delanteras que las usan para excavar la tierra. Algunas especies comen raíces y plantas mientras que otras comen artrópodos pequeños que se encuentran en el suelo. La mayoría de las especies tienen alas y pueden volar y algunas causan daño a los cultivos.

Walkingsticks

Length   2 - 8"

(Order : Phasmida)

Pseudophasma sp. (female)

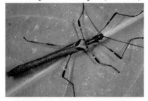

Metriophasma sp. (female)

Olinta bubastes   (female)

Walkingsticks are camouflaged insects commonly seen at night. These nocturnal herbivores show extreme morphological adaptations. The bodies are long and slender with twig-like legs and long thin antennae. At rest, the antennae and the front legs are held stiffly in front of the insect, effectively doubling its linear aspect. Colored indentations are often found at the base of the front legs, permitting them to fit snugly around the head. Most species have the brown-green-gray colors of bark, moss, and lichens. The diurnal Amazon 'fire stick' (right) is probably distasteful and exhibits warning colors. Many species are wingless and release chemicals as a secondary defense. Individuals are often found parasitized by tiny blood-sucking flies (stick-ticks) that attach to the legs and antennae and look like whitish bubbles.

La mayoría de los palitos son insectos camuflados que se mueven por la noche. Tienen la forma de ramitas y normalmente los colores naturales de corteza y musgo.

Lichenstick
Length   3 - 4"

Genus *Prisopus*
(Order : Phasmida)

Prisopus sp. (female)

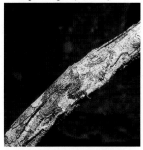

Prisopus sp. (female)

The Amazon lichenstick is a wide flattened species that is silver-gray in color to match the lichen-covered twigs on which it rests. It has the ability to curve its body around a twig (left, top) which aids in concealment. Like many walking-sticks, it has secondary defense mechanisms that come into play if the camouflage fails. If disturbed, the lichenstick will spread its hind wings (left, bottom) in an apparent startle display. The blue of the wings contrasts greatly with the rest of the body and may serve to make a predator hesitate or call off its attack. In addition, finger-like projections at the tip of the abdomen suggest that a chemical may be released at the same time that the colors are being exhibited. These insects are sometimes attracted to lights.

El palito líquen (derecha) es ancho y plano. Tiene el color gris como camuflaje, pero puede revelar alas azules cuando lo amenaza el peligro (izquierda, bajo). Es probable que también tenga químicos con mal sabor.

Mantids

Length   .5 - 6"   **(Order : Mantodea)**

Stenophylla   cornigera

Acontista sp.

Stagmatoptera   binotata

Mantids are fierce predators that slowly stalk their prey or that ambush them from strategically selected positions. The triangular head and raptorial front legs covered with sharp spines make them easy to identify, even if they have extreme morphological adaptations. The mantid fauna of the Amazon Basin is diverse and shows many unusual species. The dragon mantid (left, top) is barely over an inch long, but with the looks of an 'Alien'. Other species are almost moth-like in appearance and less than an inch long. A wide variety are mimetic, with immature forms resembling ants or adults that imitate leaves. One of the most unusual is green and white, with the bubbly appearance of a fungus (right).

Los mántidos son depredadores feroces que cazan insectos. Tienen cabezas triangulares y las patas delanteras con muchas espinas. Algunas especies parecen dragones (izquierda, arriba), hormigas y hongos (derecha).

Leaf Mantids

Length   1 - 4"

(Order : Mantodea)

Acanthops tuberculata (m.)

Choeradodis stalli (female)

Metilia brunneri   (male)

Leaf-mimicking mantids are fairly common in the rainforest, but often go unnoticed due to their incredible camouflage. Like the katydids, they imitate a wide variety of leaf shapes and colors. In many cases, specialized behaviors such as a slow swaying manner of moving contributes to the effectiveness of the disguise. In some species like *Acanthops* (right), the insect will become limp if disturbed and slowly dangle from its perch, with only the slightest of movements as if it were a leaf about to drop off. In its normal resting posture, the front legs are held around the head, concealing its characteristic triangular shape. Others like the large, green *Choeradodis stalli* (left) have evolved morphological modifications that aid in concealment. The early stages of several species are excellent ant mimics.

Hay muchas especies de mántidos que imitan hojas. Tienen una gran variedad de colores y formas como las verdaderas hojas del bosque. Tienen también comportamientos especiales.

Lichen Mantids   Genus *Liturgusa*
Length   1 - 2"   **(Mantodea : Mantidae)**

Lichen mantids are also commonly known as bark or crab mantids. The latter name comes from their ability to move laterally with incredible rapidity. Bark mantid is used because they are often found on the bark of tree trunks where they blend in so well. All parts of the body are mottled tones of gray or green that perfectly match the lichens and moss found on so many forest trees. The bodies are quite flattened and the mantids hold themselves closely appressed to

Liturgusa sp.

the trunk, thus eliminating any shadow that might be cast. The front legs are typically held forward and close to the body when these mantids are at rest. This type of camouflage requires the selection of the correct matching background (right). Lichen mantids are typical 'sit and wait' predators that prey upon flies, moths, and other small insects that walk within their reach. Little is known of the biology of this group, including the shape and size of their egg case or ootheca.

Los mántidos líquen son depredadores que se encuentran en la corteza de los árboles que están cubiertos con líquenes. Se mueven con una rapidez extrema, y a menudo en una manera lateral. Comen moscas y otros insectos pequeños.

Cockroaches

Length   1 - 4"

(Order : Blattaria)

Euphyllodromia sp.

Blaberus sp.

There are over 1,200 species of cockroaches in South and Central America that inhabit a wide variety of ecological niches and exhibit an array of behaviors. Nocturnal species tend to be soft, flattened, and brownish, while diurnal species are more hardened and colorful. Some like the genus *Paratropes* (right) show impressive coloration. All roaches have a greasy texture due to a layer of wax on the outside of the cuticle which helps them to conserve moisture. The giant cockroaches (genus *Blaberus*)(left) are the largest known species, approaching four inches. Small, vividly pigmented species in the genus *Euphyllodromia* (left) are often seen during the day on foliage. Many roaches are mimetic and resemble wasps, beetles, and even lightning bugs.

Las cucarachas son muy diversas en los trópicos. Las especies nocturnas son planas, suaves, y de color café. Las diurnas son duras y a menudo tienen colores brillantes. La cucaracha gigante alcanza una largura de cuatro pulgadas.

Queen, workers, and soldiers
of *Nasutitermes* sp.

Termites

Length   .25 - .75"

(Order : Isoptera)

Nest of *Nasutitermes* sp.

Nasutitermes sp. soldiers

Termites are a ubiquitous and visible component of tropical forest ecosystems. They are essential in the nutrient recycling process and increase the sparse fertility of tropical soils through feeding on dead plant material. They also serve as the main food source for animals such as anteaters, while their nests are used as shelters by a variety of birds and other animals. Nasute termites (genus *Nasutitermes*), are named for the tube-like projection (nasute) on the head of the soldiers. A sticky liquid and skin irritant is squirted from these tubes onto attackers. Their nests are usually arboreal and rounded, with dark 'lines' or covered galleries leading out from them to food sources. The nest material or carton is formed from chewed wood, saliva, and fecal material.

Los comejenes o las hormigas blancas hacen un papel importante en la renovación de los nutrientes. El género Nasutitermes hacen nidos redondos en los árboles y tienen 'soldados' con tubos en la cabeza que tiran chorros pegasosos.

True Bugs

Length   .5 - 2.5"

(Order : Hemiptera)

Leptoscelis pallida

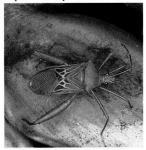

Notocyrtus sp.

The true bugs have outer wings that are leathery at the base and membranous towards the tip. In addition, the mouthparts consist of a beak designed for sucking liquids. In plant-feeding species, the beak is thin and needle-like. In predatory species, the beak is thick and substantial and can inflict a painful bite. The diversity of this order is enormous and size, shape, and color vary tremendously, especially in the tropics. Commonly seen groups are the stink bugs, assassin bugs, leaf-footed bugs, plant bugs, seed bugs, and flat bugs. Some species have spectacular colors and adornments. The bull's horn bug (right) has a pair of large horns on the back. Leaf-footed bugs have large flaps on the hind legs. Some species are excellent ant and bee mimics (left).

Chinches o hemípteros tienen alas que son duras en la base y membranosas en los extremos. Comen una dieta líquida (de las plantas o de los animales) que chupan por un pico delgado.

Stink Bugs

Length   .5 - 1.25"   **(Hemiptera : Pentatomidae)**

Edessa rufomarginata

Edessa sp.

Arvelius alboornatus

Stink bugs are true bugs whose name derives from repugnatorial glands that release a foul and distinctive odor when disturbed. They have a characteristic 'broad-shouldered' look with a large triangular plate (scutellum) between the wings. In some species, the female has been observed to guard her cluster of barrel-like eggs or newly-hatched nymphs. Immatures often stay together in groups on their foodplant. There are more than a thousand species distributed through-out the Amazon and South America.

The shield bugs are rounded and humped, with a scutellum that covers the entire back. They are sometimes placed taxonomically in the family Scutelleridae. Some species are outrageously colored with bright pigments and patterns (right).

Las conchuelas tienen glándulas que producen un mal olor. Tienen la forma característica de un escudo. Algunas especies (derecha) tienen patrones insólitos y colores brillantes.

Kissing Bugs

Length   .75 - 1.25"

Subfamily *Triatominae*
(Hemiptera : Reduviidae)

Engorged *Rhodnius* sp. nymph

Rhodnius sp. adult

Kissing bugs belong to the subfamily of assassin bugs called blood-sucking conenoses. They feed on mammalian blood, often using human hosts. They are nocturnal and tend to feed around the mouth. These insects are vectors of Chagas' disease. Also called American trypanosomyasis, the causal agent is a protozoan (*Trypanosoma cruzi*). It is passed from the feces of the bug into the bloodstream of the host during feeding, often through scratching. The bodies of kissing bugs are flattened unless engorged with blood. They are often banded, with an abdomen that sticks out on the sides beyond the wings. There is a long, conical head with two bulging eyes and a large beak. Kissing bugs hide under pieces of bark and often in the overlapping layers of roof thatch.

Las chirimachas son chinches asesinos que chupan sangre. Tienen un cuerpo allanado, ojos saltones, una cabeza larga y cónica, y un pico grande. Son portadores de la enfermedad mortal de Chagas.

Bee Killers
Length   .5 - 1"   **(Hemiptera : Reduviidae)**

Bee killers belong to the assassin bug family. They are 'sit and wait' predators that will feed on almost any insect prey whose size they can handle, but often seem to specialize on bees. The stingless bees (genus *Trigona*) seem to be especially susceptible. These bugs take up position on flowers and foliage to wait for a prey item to crawl or fly by. Stingless bees are an easy target because they build a tube-like entrance to their nest which requires them to hover before

Calliclopius nigripes

entering. While the bee maintains the same position hovering, the assassin bug grabs it with its front legs and quickly inserts its beak in its body. The injection of certain enzymes quickly renders the bee, and other prey, motionless and paralyzed. In Central America, predation by bee killers has been documented to wipe out entire colonies of stingless bees over a season. The bugs evidently have excellent eyesight, but are also attracted by chemical signals released by the bees.

'Mata abejas' son especies de chinches asesinos que son depredadores con una especialización en abejas como presa. Atacan las abejas sin aguijón con mucha frecuencia. Algunas veces estos chinches se parecen las mismas abejas.

Passion Vine Bugs

Genus *Anisoscelis*

Body Length   .5 - .75"

(Hemiptera : Coreidae)

Anisoscelis sp. nymph

Anisoscelis sp.

Among the most spectacular of the true bugs are those that feed on the passion vines (*Passiflora* spp.). These belong to the family of leaf-footed bugs which are so named because of large, flattened expansions on the hind legs. In most cases, the leg flaps are plain and dull-colored, but in passion vine bugs they are bright flags with red, orange, yellow, blue, and black. Each species has its own color combination. The bright pigments have probably evolved as warning coloration. These bugs feed on the juices of passion vines and some other plants by piercing the stem with their long, thin beaks. Although these plants contain poisonous compounds as a protection against feeding by herbivores, the bugs tolerate and use them for their own protection.

Los chinches de granadilla tienen las patas traseras con 'banderas' de colores vibrantes (izquierda y derecha). Los cuerpos también tienen mucho color. Estos colores sirven para avisarles a los depredadores que hay mal sabor.

Leafhoppers and Planthoppers

Length   .25 - 1"   **(Homoptera : Cicadellidae / Flatidae)**

Lissocarta sp.

Dilobopterus sp.

Poikilloptera phalaenoides

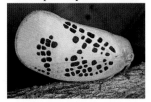

Leafhoppers are small, streamlined insects usually a half inch or less in length. They have a double row of spines on the hind leg which is a key taxonomic character. The wasphopper (left top, right) is a spectacular mimic in the leafhopper group. It is yellow and brown and matches a common neotropical paper wasp. When disturbed, the wasphopper takes flight, hovering around foliage in a wasp-like manner. It eventually lands, but keeps the wings open (right) in the posture of its wasp model. Flatid planthoppers (left bottom) are similar, but slightly larger and more wedge-shaped in appearance. They sometimes gather in groups at the end of plant stems or along them. The adults and young of both groups suck plant juices through thin beaks.

Las chicharritas son pequeños insectos que se encuentran en plantas donde chupan el jugo. Una especie (izquierda arriba y derecha) se parece a una avispa. Otras (izquierda bajo) existen en grupos en las plantas.

Wax-Tailed Planthoppers

Length   1 - 2"   **(Homoptera : Fulgoridae)**

Fulgorid planthoppers seem to provide surprises at both ends of the body. In some species, the area in front of the head may be extended into a long, irregularly shaped 'snout' or even a false head (lanternfly). In the wax-tailed

Pterodictya reticulata

hoppers, white feathery plumes of wax emanate from the tip of the abdomen. In the red-dotted planthopper (*Lystra lanata*)(right), the wax trailers are fairly short and upturned. They are usually not much longer than the length of the body (.75-1") itself. The reticulate planthopper (*Pterodictya reticulata*)(left) is slightly larger (1-1.25") and has longer, more extensive wax plumes. Wax-tailed hoppers are commonly found resting vertically on tree trunks. The purpose of the wax trailers may be to misdirect attack, leaving a predator with fragments of wax as the hopper flutters off to a new perch. If broken off, the wax will grow anew as the insect continues feeding on its copious liquid diet.

Los saltadores con colas de cera se encuentran verticalmente en los troncos de los árboles. El saltador con manchas rojas (derecha) tiene colitas cortas, pero el saltador reticulata (arriba) tiene colitas más extensivas. Estas colitas se rompen fácilmente, pero crecen otra vez como el insecto sigue comer.

Lanternfly

Genus *Fulgora*

Length   3"

(Homoptera : Fulgoridae)

Fulgora laternaria

Fulgora graciliceps

The lanternfly is one of the Amazon's most bizarre insects. Also known as the alligator bug, dragon-headed bug, and peanut-headed bug, this insect is neither a fly nor a bug. It belongs to the planthopper group and is very closely related to the cicada. Several similar appearing species are found in northern South America and Central America, none of which can bite or sting as is widely believed by natives. The apparent 'head' of this insect is actually an air-filled structure that has evolved in front of the true head. The pigmentation creates the impression of a face, with eyes and a row of teeth. The lanternfly also has eyespots on its hind wings which can be suddenly revealed in a startle display (left). Lanternfly is used because scientists believed it to be luminescent like a firefly, although this is not the case.

La chicharra machaca es un insecto con una cabeza falsa que parece un lagarto con dientes para intimidar a sus enemigos. No es venenosa y no puede picar ni hacer daño a los humanos.

Ornate Hoppers
Length   1 - 2"

Superfamily *Fulgoroidea*
(Homoptera : Fulgoridae)

Scaralis sp.

Aracynthus sanguineus

Aracynthus sanguineus

Ornate hoppers are cicada-like insects with bright colors and pigments on the hind wings and abdomen. These colors are usually hidden, but may be employed in startle displays or to confuse or intimidate predators. It is also possible that they function much in the same way as the colorful hind wings of some grasshoppers. While in flight, these insects show very obvious, noticeable colors. However, immediately upon landing the pigmented portions are concealed, giving the impression that the insect has disappeared.

The ornate hoppers feed on plant juice by inserting their slender beak into the vascular system. They do not bite or sting humans. They are often found at night attracted to lights.

Los saltadores ornados son un grupo relacionado a las chicharras. Tienen colores brillantes en las alas traseras y también en el cuerpo. Normalmente estes colores están escondidos pero se puede verlos cuando está amenazado o volando.

Treehoppers

Length   .25 - 1"

(Homoptera : Membracidae)

Heteronotus sp.

Membracis foliata

Treehoppers have some of the most bizarre shapes of any insects. The area behind the head (pronotum) in most species is extended or curved into elaborate and fanciful designs, the exact purpose of which is unknown. The unique shapes shown by these tiny creatures may in itself be a protective mechanism rendering them unrecognizable to predators as an edible item. The thorn 'bug' (*Umbonia crassicornis*)(right) imitates a plant spine. Other species may look like tiny spaceships or have flattened, bicolored bodies (left). Treehoppers feed on plant juices with a long, thin beak. They often occur in clusters and some species exhibit parental care. They excrete large amounts of liquid and are often 'tended' and protected by ants which feed on these excretions.

Los saltadores o pulgas de los árboles tienen formas increíbles, desde espinas (derecha) hasta naves espaciales. Chupan el jugo de plantas y se encuentran a menudo con hormigas que los protegen. Son menos de una pulgada en largura.

Ants

Length   .2 - 1.25"   **(Hymenoptera : Formicidae)**

Pseudomyrmex gracilis

Ectatomma tuberculatum

Pachycondyla villosa

Ants are a ubiquitous and important component of tropical rainforests. With termites, they may form as much as one-third of all the animal biomass in non-flooded Amazon forests. Studies have shown a single tree to contain more than 40 species, and estimate that more than eight million individuals can be found in one hectare of Amazonian rainforest soil. There are nearly 9,000 described species, over a third of which occur in Central and South America. Species of the genus *Pseudomyrmex* inhabit plant structures, sometimes living mutualistically as with bull's horn acacias. Solitary kelep ants (left center) are often seen on shrubs where they forage for small insects and nectar. The cobra ant (left bottom) can be recognized by its golden pubescence and long, narrow appearance. Relatives of cork-head ants are often found in groups on tree trunks (right).

Hay más de 9,000 especies de hormigas en el Nuevo Mundo. Viven en colonias desde docenas hasta millones de individuales.

Army Ants   Genus *Eciton*
Length   .5 - .75"   (Hymenoptera : Formicidae)

There are over 150 species of army ants found in South and Central America, with *Eciton bruchelli* one of the most widespread and abundant in the Amazon Basin. Colonies can be huge and number over a million. Members are commonly seen by the thousands running 8-10 abreast as they forage along forest trails. Soldiers (right) have large, curving jaws and bigger heads than the others. They feed mostly on arthropods that they overpower through sheer numbers then cut up and take back to the colony.

Eciton sp.

Army ants exhibit cyclic behavior with a nomadic and stationary phase. When stationary, the queen is bloated with eggs and may lay 300,000 in one week. The colony forms a bivuoac with the workers forming a large protective mass around the queen. As new larvae hatch and need to be fed, worker and soldier ants fan out or form raiding columns that search for food. During this nomadic phase the bivuoac is moved nightly.

Las cazadoras son hormigas que tienen colonias con más de un millón de miembros. Los soldados (derecha) tienen mandíbulas grandes y curvas. Columnas (arriba) de cazadoras cazan, matan, y comen insectos por la selva.

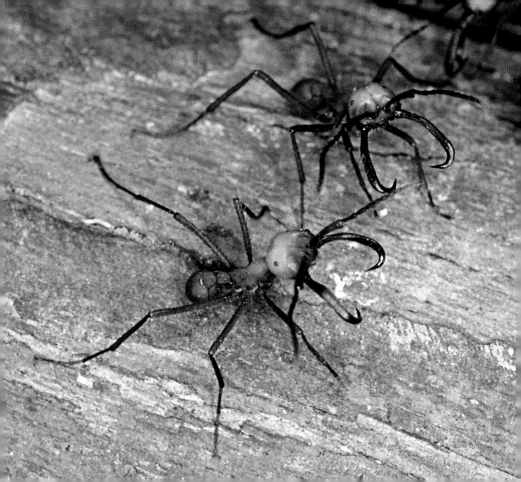

Leafcutter Ants   Genus *Atta*
Length   .25 - .75"   (Hymenoptera : Formicidae)

Leafcutter ants and army ants are those that most visitors to the tropics will see and remember. True leafcutters are found in the genera *Atta* and *Acromyrmex*. Also known as gardening or fungus-growing ants, they are found throughout Latin America and into the southern United States. Lines of foraging workers (right) are difficult to overlook in the forest as they trudge along carrying their burdens of freshly-cut pieces of leaves, stems, or flowers. They leave distinct crescent-shaped scars on the foliage they've cut. The genus *Atta* makes under-

Surface refuse of *Atta* sp. nest

ground nests where a fungus is cultivated on the leaf fragments in subterranean chambers. The ants harvest and feed on structures produced from the hyphae of the fungus. Freshly excavated soil may be dumped on the surface (left) along with dried leaves and other nest 'litter'. Some nests may have more than a million members and extend for an acre underground. Winged reproductives emerge periodically.

Los curuhuinses son hormigas que cortan hojas de plantas. Traen los pedazos a un nido subterráneo donde cultivan un hongo. Comen ciertas estructuras que el hongo produce. Se puede encontrar filas de los trabajadores de los curuhuinses en el bosque, llevando sus pedacitos de hojas recién cortados.

Giant Hunting Ants   Subfamily *Ponerinae*
Length   .75 - 1.25"   (Hymenoptera : Formicidae)

The lesser giant hunting ant (*Paraponera clavata*) and the greater giant hunting ants (*Dinoponera* spp.) are common inhabitants of the Amazon rainforest. The former is the most aggressive and smaller, only reaching about .75" in length. The latter includes *D. gigantea* which can get up to 1.25" in length and is the largest ant in the world. Both genera possess an extremely painful sting that has earned them the nickname of bullet ants. Reports of severe pain

Paraponera clavata

and fever that last for days following a sting are probably exaggerated, although in some susceptible individuals reactions might be severe. These ants typically live in small colonies of about a hundred individuals in nests excavated at the bases of trees. They are often seen on foliage, tree trunks, and in the leaf litter of the forest floor. They readily feed on sap and at the extra-floral nectaries of plants. The lesser giant hunting ant is widespread throughout Central and South America, while the greater giant hunting ant is found mainly in the Amazon Basin.

Estas hormigas cazadoras gigantes se llaman izula y son las más grandes del mundo. Tienen una picadura dolorosa pero no es mortal. Viven en pequeñas colonias con aproximademente cien miembros.

Orchid Bees   ## Subfamily *Euglossinae*

Length   .5 - 1.5"   **(Hymenoptera : Apidae)**

The orchid or emerald bees are probably the most spectacular of neotropical bees. Many of the more than 200 species are metallic green, blue, or purple (right), although some resemble large hairy bumblebees (below). All orchid bees have extremely long tongues, while the males also have an expanded area on the hind leg. The five genera of euglossine bees include: *Euglossa*, *Eulaema*, *Eufriesea*, *Exaerete*, and *Aglae*.

Eulaema cingulata w. pollen

Males are attracted to orchid flowers where they obtain chemicals which are scraped off with the front feet. They are transferred from the front legs to the hind legs as the bee hovers. These chemicals may be used in mate choice by the females which are attracted to group displays (leks) of the males. Pollination is effected by the males, which carry large packets of pollen (left) from one plant to the next. The coevolution of orchid and bee has led to ingenious adaptations for attaching and removing the pollen packets.

Estas abejas metálicas polinizan orquídeas. Las abejas machos consiguen químicos de las flores que son usado en selección sexual. Grupos de machos atraen las hembras que escogen sus parejas. Paquetes de polen se pegan a las abejas que las llevan a la próxima planta orquídea.

Stingless Bees   Tribe *Meliponini*
Length   .25 - .75"   **(Hymenoptera : Apidae)**

There are close to 200 species of stingless bees in the New World tropics. They are so named because they have vestigial stingers and must rely on other methods of defense. This includes swarming enemies and biting and pinching with the mandibles, and in the case of the 'spitfire' or *cagafogo* (*Trigona flaveola*) regurgitating a caustic liquid onto the skin of an attacker. Stingless bees generally resemble honeybees, but are smaller and vary in color. They do have a flattened tibia with hairs that make a pollen basket on the hind leg. Colonies usually contain at least several hundred adults, although in the genus *Melipona* there may be several thousand while in the genus *Trigona* (right) as many as 80,000 adults. Nests may be subterranean or built in hollow trees, often with a tube-like entrance (left). They are constructed of mud, resins, feces, and even fungi. The diet consists mainly of pollen and nectar, which in some cases (right), is taken by chewing a hole in the flower.

Stingless bee nest entrance

Las arambasas son abejas sin aguijón. Usan sus mandíbulas para defender sus nidos. Las colonias tienen entre 500 y 80,000 adultos. Se encuentran a menudo en la tierra o en árboles vacíos. Los nidos frecuentemente tienen una entrada que es un tubo hecho de resina (arriba). Comen nectar y polen.

Paper Wasps   Subfamily *Polistinae*
Length   .5 - 1.5"   (Hymenoptera : Vespidae)

These social wasps tend to live in small colonies that are ruled over by a single or several queens. Most colonies range from a few dozen to a few hundred individuals, although some which have persisted for years may have several thousand wasps. Polistes paper wasps (Genus *Polistes*) occur worldwide and have more than 80 neotropical species. They live in small colonies on a nest that consists of one open paper comb attached by a supporting stalk. Coloration varies but frequently includes yellow and brown or yellow and black.

The polybia paper wasps (Genus *Polybia*) are found throughout the Amazon Basin with more than 50 neotropical species. They vary greatly in color and pattern, but tend to construct distinctively-shaped nests for which they are often named. The bell wasp (*Chartergus chatarius*), forms a large (3-5') gray, bell-shaped nest that is often visible from rivers or lakes hanging high in the branches of adjacent trees. In the Peruvian Amazon, a small species of *Leipomeles* makes a brown nest the size and shape of an inverted funnel (right) that is often found on the underside of banana or heliconia leaves.

Estas avispas sociales viven en colonias con una o más reinas. La subfamilia Polistinae es cosmopólita y construye nidos de un solo nivel que es expuesto. El género Polybia hace nidos que tienen formas distintivas y que pueden ser muy grandes (más de un metro), como la avispa campana.

Spiders

Length   .5 - 8"   **(Arachnida : Araneae)**

Sphecotypus niger

Cupiennius sp.

Micrathena sp.

The Amazonian spider fauna is large and diverse. It encompasses many of the groups found elsewhere in the world, such as the wolf spiders (Family Lycosidae), the jumping spiders (Family Salticidae), lynx spiders (Family Oxyopidae), and orb weavers (Family Araneidae). Other groups more commonly associated with the tropics are the tarantulas (Family Theraphosidae), banana spiders (Family Ctendiae), giant crab spiders (Family Heteropodidae), and the net-throwing spiders (Family Dinopidae). Neotropical spiders have wonderful disguises to protect themselves. Some species are excellent ant mimics (left top), holding the first pair of legs forward like insect antennae. Others are extremely cryptic, resembling bits of debris or even bird droppings. These species sit with the legs drawn in tightly.

La fauna de las arañas en la cuenca amazónica es muy diversa. Algunas especies parecen hormigas y otras las heces fecales de aves. Los saltadores (derecha) son cazadores solitarios.

Tarantulas

Leg Span   3 - 8"   **(Araneae : Theraphosidae)**

Almost everyone associates the Amazon with huge insects and arachnids of all kinds. In the case of tarantulas, it is true. Specimens have been collected with leg spans greater than 10" and others with bodies as big as a man's fist. Most species however are much smaller. Tarantulas are generally large, hairy spiders with both arboreal and burrowing species. Tree dwellers use natural cavities and hiding places, and may use their silk to glue foliage together to make a shelter. Ground species use soil cavities or excavate their own, lining either with silk. Such burrows may be deep and extend for more than three feet .

Although not particularly aggressive, tarantulas have huge fangs which can be used in defense or in hunting. They feed on many types of arthropods, but also on amphibians and even birds. As an additional defense, the back legs are sometimes used to kick hairs off the abdomen into the face of an intruder. Tarantulas may live for 15-20 years and shed their skin as they grow. They are not without their own enemies and are hunted by the world's largest wasp, the tarantula hawk (*Pepsis* sp.).   These wasps sting and immobilize the spider, drag it down a burrow, and lay an egg on it which will devour its host alive.

Las tarántulas son arañas grandes y peludas que se encuentran en la tierra y también en los árboles. Son depredadores que cazan insectos, anfíbios, y aves. Pueden patear los pelos del cuerpo en la cara de un enemigo. Viven por muchos años y mudan el piel periódicamente a medida que crecen.

Golden Silk Spider   *Nephila clavipes*
Leg Span   1 - 3"   **(Araneae : Araneidae)**

This species is the only neotropical one in the genus and is found as far north as semi-tropical areas in the southeastern United States. It is the largest of orb weavers and can spin a huge web almost a yard across. The strands of the web are thick and yellow in color, hence the name of golden silk spider. The large females are commonly seen hanging head downward in the center of the web. The leg span may reach 2-3" and the body an inch and a half. They are easily recognized by the large tufts of dark hairs on all but the third pair of legs. Body color may vary, but is light on the forward portion and spotted on the posterior part. The body is elongate rather than rounded. Males are much smaller than females and tend to remain at the periphery of the web or hidden in foliage.

Golden silk spiders prey on all types of flying insects. They build their webs in forest clearings or gaps, with many webs often found clustered or adjacent to one another. The webs often host other spider species that are kleptoparasites, feeding on prey that the web or host spider has trapped. Golden silk spiders have been observed to cut distasteful butterfly species out of their webs.

La araña de seda dorada hace un gran tela que captura muchos tipos de insectos volandos. El color de la seda es amarillo. Las hembras (derecha) son mucho más grandes que los machos, y tienen grupos de pelos en todas las patas con la excepción del tercer par. Se encuentran en claros en los bosques.

Tailless Whip-Scorpion

Leg Span   3 - 8"   **(Arachnida : Amblypygida)**

Tailless whip-scorpions, also called amblypygids, belongs to the Class Arachnida along with the spiders, scorpions, pseudoscorpions, and others. It is a nocturnal predator that is more like a large spider in appearance than a scorpion. It has eight legs and a rounded, flattened body. In large specimens, the body may reach an inch across but the leg span may reach as much as eight inches. Amblypygids have a pair of fearsome spiked appendages (pedipalps) near the mouth that are used for grabbing and impaling prey. They terminate in a basket of huge spikes. The first pair of legs are very thin and much longer than the others. They are used as antennae and are often in continuous movement sensing the surrounding environment.

Amblypygids often are found on buttress roots or tree trunks in the tropical forest. They can scoot crab-like around a trunk with unbelievable speed. Although fearsome looking, they neither sting nor bite and their claw-like spikes can not break the skin. They feed on crickets, katydids, and other types of arthropods. They occur in northern South America, as well as the western and southeastern United States where they are common predators in caves.

Este arácnido parece más una araña que un escorpión. Es un depredador nocturno y caza insectos en troncos y en cuevas. No puede picar ni morder. Las patas son muy largas y se puede mover con increíble rapidez.

Millipedes   Class *Diplopoda*
Length   *1 - 4"*

Millipedes are slow-moving, commonly-seen inhabitants of tropical forests. They vary greatly in size and color, but are usually cylindrical in shape or extremely flattened. Key features separating millipedes from other non-insect arthropods are a single pair of antennae and two pairs of legs per body segment. Found during both the day and night, these creatures primarily inhabit the leaf litter of the forest floor, although they are sometimes encountered on foliage and tree trunks. They are scavengers that feed on decaying wood and decomposing vegetable matter.

Barydesmus sp.

The genus *Barydesmus* (left) (Order Polydesmida) consists of large-bodied (3-4"), flat-backed individuals found in Central America and the Amazon. At first glance, they look like small pieces of walking tire treads. The flattened, armored body serves to protect them. Other groups of millipedes have warning colors (right) that advertise their ability to release noxious chemicals.

Los milpies se mueven lentamente y son vistos fácilmente en el suelo del bosque. Algunas especies son planas como en el orden Polydesmida (arriba), mientras que otras tienen una forma cilíndrica. Comen materiales vegetales.

Centipedes

Genus *Scolopendra*

Length   2 - 10"

(Class : Chilopoda)

Centipedes are quick-moving predatory creatures that are active at night. They can be distinguished from millipedes and other non-insect arthropods by having a single pair of long antennae and only one pair of legs per body segment. The body tends to be flattened and the first pair of legs is usually modified into poison fangs that are used for injecting venom into their prey. During the day, centipedes can be found hiding under logs, bark, rocks, in rotting wood, and other sheltering refuges.

The genus *Scolopendra* has ten neotropical species, including *Scolopendra gigantea*, a species which reaches ten inches in length. Speices of *Scolopendra* are found throughout the Amazon Basin and on some of the Caribbean islands. This group has 21-23 pairs of legs. Their diet consists of insects, earthworms, and probably even small vertebrates that they are capable of overpowering. The bites of centipedes may be extremely painful, but no fatalities have been recorded.

Las escolopendras tienen diez especies en el Nuevo Mundo, incluyendo una que alcanza 10" en largura. Son depredadores que se mueven rápidamente, cazando la presa que muerden y matan con veneno. Son nocturnas y pasan el día bajo troncos, rocas, y corteza. Los miembros del género Scolopendra tienen 21 o 23 pares de patas. Comen insectos y lombrices.

Land Planarians

Length   2 - 12"

Class *Turbellaria*

(Phylum : Platyhelminthes)

The phylum of flatworms is made up of three classes consisting of the flukes, tapeworms, and the planarians. This latter group is made up of more than 3,000 species, including those triangular-headed, cross-eyed individuals that most of us observed in biology class. The majority of species are small or microscopic and live in freshwater or marine environments. However, some of the turbellarians or planarians are terrestrial in nature and live in humid tropical environments such as are found in the Amazon Basin. These species may be brightly colored (right) and get up to twelve inches in length.

The large land planarians are flat and ribbon-like and are somewhat pointed at both ends. They are typically slick and shiny looking. They move by means of tiny hairs (cilia) on the undersurface that glide over a film of mucus that is secreted. Most land planarians are predaceous and feed on small invertebrates that they secure by crawling over and entrapping with mucus. Some species swallow their prey whole, while others secrete digestive enzymes externally and then suck up the liquefied tissues.

Las planarias de tierra son ejemplos insólitos de turbelarios. Alcanzan a tener una largura de doce pulgadas y tienen colores brillantes. Son muy planos y tienen la forma de una cinta. Comen invertebrados pequeñitos que atrapan con mucosa. Se encuentra en el suelo del bosque.

Velvet Worms
Length   1 - 6"

Phylum *Onycophora*
(Onycophora : Peripatidae)

The velvet worms are a truly strange group of tropical creatures that are found throughout the world, usually in hot, humid environments. They are very similar in appearance to fossil imprints that have been found from the Cambrian period of geological history. They appear to be a cross between a caterpillar, a millipede, and a slug. However, from a taxonomic point of view, they more closely represent a cross between a segmented worm (Phylum Annelida) and the insects and arthropods (Phylum Arthropoda). They have been classified into their own small phylum, the Onycophora.

Onycophorans vary in color and have soft skin that is covered with little bumps or tubercles. This gives them a velvety appearance and hence the name. They are active mostly at night and tend to remain in sheltered places such as beneath rocks and logs. They are predaceous and feed upon small invertebrate organisms such as insects, snails, and worms. The prey is captured by shooting out a mucilaginous substance produced by slime glands near the mouth. This material can be projected for several inches and is also used as a defense.

Los onicoforos tienen piel suave de varios colores y con pequeñas protuberancias. Tienen las características de artrópodos y anélidos. Son depredadores que comen pequeños insectos y caracoles. Capturan su presa con un chorro de mucílago, que también usan como defensa.

U2

Mark Taylor

AN ORION PAPERBACK

This is a Carlton Book

First published in Great Britain in 1993 by Orion Books Ltd.
Orion House, 5 Upper St Martin's Lane, London WC2H 9EA

A CIP catalogue record for this book is available from the British Library.

ISBN 1 85797 567 7

Edited, designed and typeset by Haldane•Mason
Printed in Italy

THE AUTHOR
Mark Taylor
Mark is a rock journalist and author. He is a regular contributor to numerous British rock
magazines. This is his third book.

Contents

IntrOduction

When U2 played their first shows in Dublin in the late Seventies, no one would have believed that this shambolic quartet were destined to become the biggest band in the world. Yet, inspired by punk rock, Bono Vox, The Edge, Adam Clayton and Larry Mullen understood that rock 'n' roll wasn't just about expertise and technical know-how, but about energy, attitude and, above all, an ability to communicate.

In Bono, U2 had an extraordinary frontman who could win over even the most indifferent crowd. Over the course of their first four albums U2 built up a massive following in Europe and America, but it was at Live Aid in July 1985, during that incredible moment when Bono leapt off the stage to embrace a girl in the crowd, that the band really began to conquer the world.

Their next album, 1987's *The Joshua Tree*, went to Number 1 in Britain and America and has gone on to sell more than 14 million copies.

But rather than settling into a cosy, unadventurous niche at the top of the charts, U2 created their next album, *Rattle And Hum*, as a tribute to their rock 'n' roll heroes past and present.

Having paid their respects, U2 then forged ahead into the future with 1991's *Achtung Baby* and their massive multi-media rock 'n' roll extravaganza, Zoo TV.

U2 recently signed a record deal worth £160 million ($240 million)—the second most lucrative in the history of popular music—and can be proud that they are one of Ireland's most important exports. But neither the band nor their manager Paul McGuinness (who has been with them since 1978) will be indulging in self-congratulation—they'll be thinking about the future and how U2 is going to forge on into the next century.

Bono looks into the mists of the future.

CHAPTER 1

Early days

When a restless adolescent called Paul Hewson set up his own disco club in a Dublin schoolhouse in the early Seventies, no one could have imagined that one day the young DJ would be fronting the biggest multi-media rock 'n' roll extravaganza in the world—and indeed it would be two decades and many hard years before the club which Paul had christened "The Web" would spin out into Zoo TV.

Paul's disco venture turned out to be short-lived, but soon after its demise he heard that there was a card on the school noticeboard of Dublin's Mount Temple Comprehensive advertising for guitarists for a new band. Paul couldn't really play

guitar, but he knew that wasn't important—it was the autumn of 1976 and he had just become aware of punk. Music was no longer about expertise and technical know-how, it was about attitude, energy and the idea that anyone could do whatever they wanted. Paul decided to find out more about the new band.

Feedback is born

The request for guitarists came from a 14-year-old called Larry Mullen, who had started playing drums when he was 9 and was already a veteran of both the Artane Boys Band and the Post

Paul Hewson (aka "Bono Vox"), whose ideas were more important than expertise with a guitar.

8

Office Band. Now he had had enough of other people's bands and was determined to form his own.

In addition to leaving a card on the noticeboard, Larry approached an English-born fellow pupil named Adam Clayton. Although Adam had only been at Mount Temple for a couple of months, his wild head of blond hair, tinted glasses and Afghan coat had made everybody notice him. Larry thought Adam was the coolest kid at Mount Temple and wanted him in his band.

Luckily for Larry, Adam owned a bass guitar and agreed to go to the drummer's house for a jam with the other people who had responded to the notice. Among them were Dave Evans and his brother Dick, who had built their own guitar, and Paul Hewson, who didn't have a guitar but insisted he could play one. They

Larry Mullen, at 14 a veteran of both the Artane Boys Band and the Post Office Band.

shambled their way through a couple of Rolling Stones hits and, even though Adam couldn't really play and the Evans brothers' guitar didn't sound as good as it looked, they were all impressed by the noise they had made and officially declared themselves a band. They christened their new group Feedback and vowed to rehearse three times a week.

Lypton Village

Sixteen-year-old Paul Hewson was very excited about being in a band.

> "Adam...made up his mind at 15 or 16 that rock 'n' roll was what he was going to do."
>
> *Bono*

Adam Clayton—Larry thought him the coolest kid at Mount Temple.

His mother had died 2 years earlier and music was the only thing that even came near to soothing his overwhelming sense of loss. He frequently borrowed records from his friends and taped them on his father's reel-to-reel and, with these same friends, he helped to dream up an imaginary world that he called Lypton Village.

Fans of T Rex, David Bowie and now Patti Smith and punk, the Village felt nothing but contempt for the accepted way of Irish life which involved going down to the pub, getting married, having children, getting a job at 16 and sticking at it for the next 50 years. They hated Gaelic football and spent their time in each others' living-rooms, listening to music, painting and plotting to become famous and change the world. They avoided "normal" people and were drawn instead to those who were "different", outsiders—people to whom they referred as Virgin Prunes.

To emphasize their outsiderdom the Village gave each other new names, like Gavin Friday, Guggi, Pod, Dav.id Busarus Scott, Strongman and Dik (previously Dick

Evans). Paul was renamed Bono Vox of O'Connell Street after a hearing-aid shop on Dublin's main street (and Bono later christened Dave Evans "The Edge" on account of his sharp mind).

Bono's tenacity

Once Feedback started having regular rehearsals in the Mount Temple School Gym, it became glaringly apparent that Bono couldn't play guitar—and he couldn't sing particularly well, either. The other three thought about kicking him out, but he proved to have a tenacious spirit and began to make up for his lack of musical ability by developing his qualities as a frontman. But just when the group was improving, Bono (who was in the class above Adam and The Edge, and 2 years ahead of Larry) was offered a place at University College Dublin (UCD). His departure would have seriously

Dave Evans, later christened "The Edge" by Paul Hewson on account of his sharp mind.

affected Feedback's rehearsals and perhaps the entire future of the band. UCD, however, later discovered that Bono had failed his Irish Exam and he was sent back to Mount Temple for another unappetizing year of study.

The first gig

Soon afterwards, in the autumn of 1977, Mount Temple hosted a talent contest at the school and Feedback got the opportunity to play their first gig. They only played a 10-minute set of other bands' songs, but received a rapturous response. "We built on a spark," Bono would say later. By the time they played their second gig, they had changed their name to the Hype and Dik Evans had dropped out of the band.

U2 is christened

In March 1978, Adam was expelled from Mount Temple and decided to devote all his time and energy to the band. "Adam believed in this band before anyone else," Bono said subsequently. "Maybe it's

> ## "Adam believed in this band before anyone else."
>
> *Bono*

because he was thrown out of school and there was no other alternative, but he had made up his mind at 15 or 16 that rock 'n' roll was what he was going to do."

Adam made it his business to ring up musicians on the Dublin rock scene (like Thin Lizzy's Phil Lynott) and ask for advice on how to get gigs. It was during such a call to Steve Averill, the lead singer of one of Ireland's premier punk

Bono at an early U2 gig; "We built on a spark", he said of Feedback's rapturous reception at their first gig.

bands, the Radiators From Space, that Adam confessed that he had his doubts about calling the band the Hype. Steve Averill, who later designed the band's album covers, suggested that they should rename themselves U2 (a word so ambiguous that it might refer to a plane, submarine, battery or simply "you too"). Soon afterwards, on St Patrick's Night (March 17), the band went down to Limerick to take part in a Harp Lager-sponsored talent contest and came away with the first prize of £500 ($750) and the opportunity to do a recording session in the CBS studios.

The Radiators From Space, led by Steve Averill (on the right), who originally suggested the name 'U2'.

Developing the sound

By this time, U2 had dropped the Beach Boys covers that they had started out with and were struggling to develop a sound of their own. While Larry and Adam were learning to work together and form the backbone of the band, The Edge was progressing beyond basic blues licks and forging a unique distorted yet highly colourful style.

For his part, Bono was providing a series of improvised lyrics for their growing repertoire of songs. These included 'Cartoon World', 'The Fool' and 'Shadows And Tall Trees', but U2's most important song was one that Bono had written on his eighteenth birthday, as he sat alone in his bedroom thinking about his mother, and came to the realization that the two most important events in your life, being born and dying, have nothing to do with you—they're 'Out Of Control'.

Virgin Prunes

Inspired by U2's progress, the Village had formed their own band and called it the Virgin Prunes. It started off with Guggi and Gavin forming a bizarre sideshow (or simply just taking over from Bono) while U2 played, but quickly developed into a six-piece which included The Edge's brother Dik Evans on guitar and Dav.id as a third singer and performer (and sometimes the Prunes were augmented by Larry, Adam and The Edge, who would serve as an additional backing band). More like a theatre performance than just another rock band, the Virgin Prunes' interest was in challenging the preconceptions of their audience rather than forming a bond with them simply to entertain them.

The band gains a manager

U2's gigs were now attracting a small following, but the band had reached another crossroads. The school year was coming to an end—which meant that, unless they could turn U2 into a full-time concern, their parents would force them to find alternative careers. Desperate to save the band, its members asked Dublin's *Hot Press* magazine's Bill Graham to give them some advice. He told them to get themselves a decent manager and gave them the phone number of his friend Paul McGuinness, who worked in film production but also managed a Celtic folk rock band called Spud.

McGuinness first saw U2 at Dublin's Project Arts Theatre in May and, although he knew that they had

The Edge and Bono enjoy a post-concert beer in 1979, the year of their first success in the Irish charts.

Guggi and Dik (Evans) of the Virgin Prunes, a band inspired by U2's progress. The aim of the Virgin Prunes was to challenge the preconceptions of their audience rather than simply to provide straightforward rock entertainment.

a long, hard road ahead of them, he was impressed by Bono's efforts to communicate with the audience and decided to take them on.

The arrival of Paul McGuinness was crucial to the development of U2. He understood that rock 'n' roll was a business, not just recreation. Under his influence, over the next 6 months the band rehearsed harder than ever, played an increasing number of gigs and recorded a three-track demo with ex-Horslips bassist Barry Devlin.

In February 1979, the Project hosted a punk festival called Dark Space—24 Hours, which featured U2 and the Virgin Prunes alongside other hopefuls like Protex, DC Nien and the Vipers. The headliners at the festival were the Leeds band the Mekons and the compère was the influential British DJ John Peel. However, although the show was reviewed by a journalist from UK rock paper *New Musical Express*, U2 didn't get a mention.

The first record deal

Meanwhile, despite McGuinness's best efforts, the demo that the band had recorded with Barry Devlin hadn't inspired any major label interest. So, in the spring of 1979, U2 did a deal with CBS Ireland. They immediately recorded three tracks with producer Chas de Whalley, for their debut EP, *U23*. The three tracks were 'Out Of Control', which had become one of the central songs in their live set, 'Stories For Boys' and 'Boy/Girl'.

Uncertain as to which track should be on the A side, they made an agreement with the pioneering RTE radio DJ Dave Fanning: he would play all three songs on his rock show and let U2's fans decide which song to choose. 'Out Of Control' proved to be the most popular choice, and the EP was

Bono was determined to connect emotionally with every single member of the audience.

released in September 1979 as a limited edition of 1000 numbered copies—which quickly took them to the top of the Irish charts.

U2 in London

However, U2's chart success in the Irish Republic didn't mean much in the UK, as they were to discover when they played their first London dates towards the end of the year. The band hadn't expected to be catapulted to instant fame, but they were shocked by the indifference that greeted them. "They were strange days when you're just off the boat in a foreign land," Adam would recall. "I mean, England is a foreign land if you come from Dublin—even though I was originally English—and can make you feel very small."

Nine in the audience

But, even though U2 were playing to tiny crowds again (they played one legendary show at the Hope

and Anchor, a pub in Islington, north London, to an audience of only nine people) Bono was more determined than ever to connect emotionally with those who had bothered to turn up. If one person in the audience was left unmoved by U2, then he felt the band had failed.

What frustrated the singer most about the London music scene was that every band had to be classified by some sort of genre—rock, punk, mod, ska, heavy metal, rockabilly. Everyone had to have a label, everyone had to fit in. U2 had never fitted in—and they weren't about to start now. "London is chained in bondage," Bono said angrily in U2's first interview in the English rock press.

Competing with the showbands

By this time, U2 (like almost every other Irish rock band before them) were beginning to realize that if they were going to make it in the music business they would probably have to move to England. In the meantime, though, they were determined to leave an impression on their own country and among their targets were the hordes of bright, shiny showbands who would trot out a repertoire of

> "England is a foreign land if you come from Dublin...and can make you feel very small."
>
> *Adam*

The Edge does his best to ignore Bono's limbo dancing during a gig on the band's 1979 tour of Ireland. U2 were determined to make an impression by playing original music.

chart hits to adoring, docile audiences, thus depriving young bands of the chance to play original music.

As an experiment, U2 got themselves a Sunday night slot at a dance hall called the Garden of Eden Club in a small village 70 miles from Dublin with Cork-born singer Tony Stevens (who had been drawn into the music business after hearing an Irish showband play the Beatles' classic 'Daytripper'). Bono was determined to go for it: undaunted, he rushed on to the stage, shouted "Good evening, everyone!" and tried to convince himself and the rest of U2 that this Sunday-night crowd would get excited about 'Cartoon World' and 'Out Of Control', when all they really wanted to hear was Tony Stevens churning out old favourites. Bono worried at the time about people being lost forever to live music in the anodyne atmosphere of clubs like the Garden of Eden. "They might never see another amplifier again," he declared. "Ever!"

"When U2 started," he would say years later, "the only bands who were making any money in Ireland were the showbands who played other people's songs. Of course, at one time—when there was only Irish television—people didn't know what Gerry and the Pacemakers looked like, so they would see these guys in red suits and painted-on smiles and imagine that they were Gerry and the Pacemakers. That was the tradition, and U2 rebelled against that." But it would take the band a while to win converts to their cause.

Bono wanted to provide an alternative to the banality of trotting out a repertoire of chart hits, to save the audience from that "Garden of Eden".

> "When U2 started, the only bands who were making any money in Ireland were the showbands who played other people's songs... That was the tradition, and U2 rebelled against that."
>
> *Bono*

Island signs the band

Despite their unfavourable reception at the Garden of Eden, U2 proved that they had achieved popularity in certain parts of Ireland by winning five categories in the 1979 *Hot Press* Readers' Poll. None the less, the band entered 1980 in pretty low spirits, since they still hadn't managed to secure a major label deal. Over in London, however, U2 had an influential fan in Island Records' publicist Rob Partridge, who was doing his best to persuade the label to sign them. A&R man Bill Stewart arrived to see them play in front of a thousand people in Dublin's Stadium and, highly impressed, offered them a four-album deal.

Left: Bono, a rebel in search of a cause on a Dublin street.

Right: Rebels against tradition about to step out of the Dublin shadows.

promise of 'Out Of Control'. However, it taught U2 a valuable though hard lesson: they couldn't afford to release anything they weren't happy with.

For their first Island single, '11 O'Clock Tick Tock', the band specifically requested a collaboration with producer Martin Hannett, because

> **"The music here is enough to make you cry."**
>
> *Melody Maker*

Bono at a U2 show soon after the band were signed to Island Records by Bill Stewart—it was obviously going to be quite some time before he found what he was looking for...

CBS Ireland had just released U2's second single, 'Another Day' (again produced by Chas de Whalley), which was a pretty weak effort that failed to build on the of his work on Joy Division's *Unknown Pleasures*, an album they greatly admired. Their collaboration with him produced a similarly dark atmosphere for this first Island release. The song sounded the knell for the post-punk rock world, while also searching for answers, revealing the kind of dichotomy that would crop up again and again in U2's lyrics but never be fully resolved.

U2 in the days when you could see them at a knock-down price.

The band tours Britain

On completing the recording in Dublin's Windmill Lane Studios, U2 embarked on a long tour of Britain, playing small club dates. Bono seemed keener than ever to communicate with the crowd, staring at them, talking to them, climbing off stage and walking among them, dragging a chair into the

The Edge on vocals—no match for his guitar playing.

midst of them and frequently just asking people for a cigarette, a light or both. Some people walked out, thinking he was mad or phoney or both, but most were drawn in, fascinated by U2's haunting sound and strangely compelling singer.

While Bono was trying to communicate with the crowd

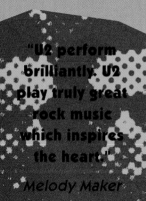

"U2 perform brilliantly. U2 play truly great rock music which inspires the heart."

Melody Maker

physically, The Edge was trying to tell them something equally important with the sound of his guitar. Martin Hannett had agreed to produce U2's debut LP, but pulled out when Joy Division's singer Ian Curtis committed suicide in May 1980—a death which sparked U2's next single, 'A Day Without Me', and marked the real advent of The Edge's echo-laden guitar sound.

Before they recorded the song, Bono kept telling The Edge that he could hear a chord repeating in his head, prompting the guitarist to go out and buy a Memory Man Deluxe echo unit. He spent the following weeks integrating the new experimental sounds into the songs that U2 had written for their debut LP, *Boy*.

The first LP

It was The Edge's ringing guitar that opened the first track on the LP, 'I Will Follow'. Filled with an almost desperate sense of yearning, the

song set the tone for the whole record, with lyrics partly inspired by the death of Bono's mother. On songs like 'I Will Follow', 'Out Of Control', 'Twilight' and the beautiful 'Into The Heart', U2 were searching, as they would search many times in the future, for something that couldn't be articulated.

In keeping with this idea of a quest, the album cover showed the face of an innocent-looking boy (Peter Rowen, the younger brother of the Virgin Prunes' Guggi) and the songs followed his journey from boyhood through the pain and discovery of adolescence to man-hood. Producer Steve Lillywhite, whose previous credits included Siouxsie and the Banshees, Ultravox and Eddie and the Hot Rods, but who was only a few years older than the band themselves, had helped U2 to come of age. *Boy*

U2 perform for an audience who will follow—but not just yet.

Bono launches into an impromptu Rod Stewart impersonation at the Lyceum.

married the bright optimism of epic pop with compellingly dark atmospherics that set it apart from any other record at the time. "The music here is enough to make you cry," one *Melody Maker* journalist wrote of *Boy*.

Blowing the Bunnymen off stage

With the LP completed, U2 returned to London in September and played what they regarded as a disastrous support slot to Echo and the Bunnymen at the Lyceum. But although they regarded it as a bad night, *Melody Maker*'s Lynden Barber, seeing the band for the first time, immediately fell in love with them and later reported that they had blown the Bunnymen off stage.

The following week, U2 were back on the same bill as the Bunnymen at the Leeds Futurama Festival

in the north of England, along with the nascent Soft Cell (best remembered for their version of Black Sabbath's track 'Paranoid') and Siouxsie and the Banshees. Although U2 had to be content with an early afternoon slot, it was a good chance to play to a large audience. "U2 perform brilliantly," enthused UK's *Melody Maker*, "U2 play truly great rock music which inspires the heart."

Afterwards an elated Bono said that he had felt like Pope John Paul. However, while U2 were happy to be making some kind of impression on England, Paul McGuinness was busy looking westward. He had already set his sights on conquering America.

Heaven up here, U2-style. By late 1980 the band's originality was receiving recognition.

CHAPTER 2

On the way up

Boy was released to widespread acclaim in October 1980, giving U2 the opportunity to build a solid fan base. Paul McGuinness had arranged an 8-day tour of America's East Coast, starting on December 5. The tour had been put together by Frank Barsalona, who was president of the world's most powerful rock agency, Premier Talent.

The first show of the tour ended up being cancelled, so U2 made their American début at New York's Ritz, in front of a 2200-capacity crowd, who didn't really want to watch a band—they just wanted to dance. At first only a hundred or so people were watching but, song by song, U2 won over a couple of hundred more, until the ones at the back wondered what they were missing out on and started watching too. Eventually, U2 had captivated the whole place. Frank Barsalona was so excited that he ran to their dressing-room to shake every one of them by the hand and promise them his unequivocal support.

Bono, looking to the stars and beyond, to the United States, to increase U2's rising stock.

> **"John Lennon changed my way of seeing things."**
>
> *Bono*

The trip was marred 2 days later, however, when one of the band's early heroes, John Lennon, was shot dead in the street outside his New York apartment. "John Lennon changed my way of seeing things," Bono would say later.

On the road in the USA

Boy was released in the States in January, but only after the photograph of Peter Rowen had been replaced by a shot of the band—there were worries about the possible gay or paedophile connotations

The Edge and his guitar—the creative force behind the U2 sound. The start of the band's first US tour, in December 1980, was marred by the death of John Lennon, one of their early heroes.

had walked into the band's dressing room in Portland, Oregon, smiled nicely at them and walked out again or whether Bono had simply mislaid it *en route* to Seattle was uncertain. The fact that the singer had also lost his passport and a considerable amount of money was incidental, since he never managed to write a proper set of lyrics for the next album and ended up improvising them in the studio.

U2 weaving their magic on American audiences early in 1981.

of showing a picture of a young boy's naked chest. The album got a rave review in *Rolling Stone* magazine and scraped into *Billboard*'s Top 100. Meanwhile, a sell-out show at London's Lyceum in February was evidence of U2's increasing popularity in England.

In March U2 set out on their first major US tour, which consisted of a solid 3 months on the road apart from a 10-day break to record their next single, 'Fire', in the studio in the Bahamas that Island signings frequently used.

By the time the band met up with producer Steve Lillywhite, Bono no longer had the notes and lyrics which he had made for their next LP and which had been travelling across America with him in his briefcase. Whether the case was taken by the two good-looking girls who

Bono in enigmatic mood in Ireland during the early Eighties.

The making of October

The making of U2's second LP, *October*, was a struggle from start to finish. For the previous 2 years, Bono, Larry, The Edge and various members of the Village had been involved in a Christian sect called Shalom and it was becoming increasingly difficult for them to reconcile rock 'n' roll with their faith. While U2 were on the road, various members of the Virgin Prunes had been pressurized into making a choice between rock 'n' roll and Christianity. Guggi and Gavin chose the Prunes. As U2 travelled across America and Europe during the first half of 1981, there was a visible gap between Adam—who wasn't

The 1980–1 US tour: Larry, Bono and The Edge, with Adam out on a limb.

interested in organized religion but totally believed in U2—and the other three members of the band.

In addition to these difficulties, U2 were also battling against time. Once they had finished their touring commitments, they ended up with a woefully inadequate 3 weeks in which to prepare the record before they were due to go into the Windmill Lane studio with Steve Lillywhite. Their confusion and desperation manifested themselves on the record itself—not least on the opening track, 'Gloria'. "I try to sing this song," sang Bono, and that is literally what he was doing as he made up the words while standing at the microphone.

Although *October* was a disappointing follow-up to *Boy*, both 'Gloria' and 'Tomorrow' (which was a hymn for Bono's late mother)

October-era U2: revealing the band's deep bond with and affection for their Irish homeland.

32

were fully realized expressions of the spiritual alienation that lay at the heart of U2. The latter song, which featured the lilting sound of Vinnie Kilduff's uilleann pipes, also revealed a profound sense of physical alienation from the homeland to which the band was so attached.

In the UK charts

A couple of months before *October* was released in October 1981, U2 entered the UK charts for the first time with 'Fire'. Reaching Number 35, the single didn't exactly set the hit parade alight, but it was enough to earn them a television appearance on BBC's prime-time slot for popular music, *Top of the Pops*. Dressed in black with distinctively undistinctive haircuts, U2 didn't look as if they were about to do battle at the top of the charts with New Romantics like Spandau Ballet and Duran Duran. Later they prided themselves on the fact that they were one of the few bands to

appear on the programme whose single dipped in the following week!

Staying home

By this time U2 felt completely removed from the English music scene, which seemed to be full of either the New Romantic cocktail set or groups who had been inspired by punk but appeared to hanker after the kind of rock stardom that bands like the Sex Pistols

and the Clash had set out to destroy. Although Adam later confessed that he wouldn't have minded going to Rusty Egan's Club for Heroes, which was London's hippest club at the time, the fact that U2 had decided to remain in Dublin gave them the increasingly

U2 make their *Top of the Pops* debut with 'Fire' in August 1981. The record reached Number 35 in the UK charts.

valuable perspective of outsiders. Towards the end of the summer they co-headlined a show at Slane Castle, a magnificent old building on the banks of the River Boyne in County Meath, with Thin Lizzy, which was a big deal for them given Lizzy's standing and Slane's burgeoning reputation for hosting Ireland's biggest rock shows.

Yet Bono, The Edge and Larry still hadn't reconciled rock 'n' roll with their faith and no longer knew whether they wanted to be in a band. Just before they were due to embark on a month-long US tour, the three of them told McGuinness that they couldn't go ahead with it. McGuinness patiently reminded them of the commitments they had made to U2, and the dilemma was temporarily resolved.

Although *October* had failed to reach *Billboard*'s Top 100, U2 were

Bono: trying to balance the competing demands of Christianity and rock.

Bono and his wife Alison pictured in 1987, 5 years after they were married.

given their first taste of America's arena-land when Premier Talent put them on the J. Geils band tour. Their following grew steadily throughout the first half of 1982, both in the United States and in Europe, where they headlined a series of festivals throughout the summer that year.

Making commitments

In August, Bono married his longtime girlfriend, Alison, and although he was still committed to Christianity he had partly resolved the conflict that he had felt between Shalom and rock 'n' roll. His new lease of life could be heard in the single 'A Celebration', U2's only release of 1982, where he sang about not being overcome by the powers that be. The Edge, however, was still feeling the pull between his conscience (and commitment to the Shalom group) and his ego (and desire to play rock 'n' roll in U2). When Bono returned from his honeymoon, The Edge told him that he was going to have to take 2 weeks out of U2 to decide his future. It was crisis point: if the guitarist decided to commit himself fully to Christianity, then Bono felt that there was no point in any of them continuing in U2 and they would break up the band.

However, within a couple of days, The Edge had realized that being a Christian and playing in a rock 'n' roll band weren't mutually exclusive. He decided to go forward with U2 and from that moment had no doubts.

Rather than looking inwards, U2 opened their eyes to the outside world. Every way they turned that

year, they saw war: the British-Argentinian conflict in the Falklands, the struggle of Solidarity in Poland, the continued presence of the United States in Central America, and the increasing bloodshed in the Middle East, South Africa and on U2's own doorstep in Northern Ireland. Overshadowing all this was the threat of nuclear war, a topic which Bono had already touched on in 'A Celebration'. All these issues and dilemmas were uppermost in the minds of the band when they went into Windmill Lane studio in early autumn 1982. They started working on an album that would represent a mix of their spiritual energy and a new sense of social and political awareness.

The next album

Ever since *October*, Steve Lillywhite had been trying to help U2 to find a

Bono beneath the blood red shadow cast by *War*.

> ## "The talk during *War* all the time was the Clash."
>
> ### *Steve Lillywhite*

new producer. They had considered collaborating with Chris Thomas (whose credits included the Beatles, the Sex Pistols and the Pretenders) and Sandy Pearlman (who had produced the Clash's second LP, *Give 'Em Enough Rope*), but in the end it was Lillywhite who guided U2 through *War*.

This time round, U2 had a clearer idea of the kind of sound they were looking for. Steve Lillywhite later recalled that "the talk during *War* all the time was the Clash". Unlike the shinily self-indulgent New Romantic and synth bands whose records were sitting at the top of the charts during 1982, the Clash had managed to document the real world and slap people in the face with their recent LP, *Combat Rock*. In an album that Bono would later describe as "a reaction to the cocktail-set mentality", U2 decided to strip their sound down, do away with the atmospherics that had been such an important part of *Boy* and *October*, and go for something much more abrasive and hard-hitting.

But before the release of *War* came 'New Year's Day', a single that was part love song and part call to arms. Bono revealed later that it was inspired by the Polish Solidarity movement and, in particular, its leader Lech Walesa, who had been imprisoned and separated from his wife. Released on January 1, 1983, 'New Year's Day' was a pulsing, perfectly crafted single that soared into the upper echelons of the British charts, giving U2 their first Top 10 hit at Number 10.

Number 1

It became obvious exactly how much of a live following U2 had built up when *War* was released a couple of months later and shot straight into the UK charts at Number 1. The cover was a photograph of the same boy who had appeared on their début LP, but he looked bruised and nervous, his arms thrown behind his head as though in surrender, rather than the youthful innocent of 3 years before.

The album began on a provocative note with the highly charged 'Sunday Bloody Sunday'. The title referred to two specific occasions in Irish history when civilians had been gunned down by British soldiers, the first time at a Gaelic football match in Dublin's Croke Park in 1920 and the second on the streets of Derry in 1972. John Lennon had written about the second incident in a highly emotive song which had also been called 'Sunday Bloody Sunday' and was included on his and Yoko Ono's 1972 LP, *Sometime in New York City*. But U2's song wasn't as black and white as Lennon's; their 'Sunday Bloody Sunday' wasn't a comment on the physical violence of Northern Ireland, but (like 'New Year's Day' and many of the other songs on *War*), was a call for love and understanding.

Although *War* was criticized for being too bombastic and blatantly

The youthful boys of 1980 grown into the troubled men of 1983's *War*.

rockist, there was a sense of experimentation on tracks like 'Two Hearts Beat As One' (which was essentially a dance track), the haunting 'Drowning Man' (featuring Steve Wickham on violin), 'Surrender' (which included a solo trumpeter and Kid Creole's female backing vocalists, the Coconuts) and the gentle '40', which closed the album with the same question as 'Sunday Bloody Sunday'.

The tours sell out

When U2 set out on a sold-out tour of Britain, 'Sunday Bloody Sunday' became a central part of their performance. "Coming from Dublin, we were very nervous about performing a song like 'Sunday Bloody Sunday' in Belfast," said The Edge. "The first time we played it, Bono said, 'This is a song about what's going on up here. If you don't

Bono beneath the white flag, symbol of anti-nationalism and peace.

like it we won't play it again.' The place went wild and we had no doubts from then on."

Bono repeatedly stressed that 'Sunday Bloody Sunday' was not a rebel song and would wave a white flag (a symbol of anti-nationalism and peace) and hand it to the audience at some point during the song. He later explained that he had been sick of the green, white and gold Irish flag, sick of the Union Jack and the stars and stripes, sick of any flag that people were prepared to die for: "I wished the colours could be drained from them, and just leave the white flag."

The British dates were followed by a 3-month tour of America, which had also sold out long before U2 arrived. Although they were playing bigger venues now, Bono was still as anxious to reach people as he had been when the band first started. The days when he could pull up a chair and sit among the audience might be long gone, but

"Coming from Dublin, we were very nervous about performing a song like 'Sunday Bloody Sunday' in Belfast... The place went wild and we had no doubts from then on."

The Edge

he solved this by either pulling someone out of the crowd to dance with him (a move that had been instigated by Bruce Springsteen) or

Bono in concert, with the symbolic white flag draped round his mic stand.

Above: Bono and Adam spread the message in *War* to American fans.

leaving the stage and making his way out among them, teetering along ledges, climbing into balconies, shinning up scaffolding and once even taking a 20-foot leap down into the front rows.

Climbing to the top

The response to U2 was now wilder than they had ever dared to dream about and it seemed to make it even more valid when

musicians that they truly respected, like Bruce Springsteen and the Who's John Entwistle, started turning up at their shows. At the end of May 1983, the band got the chance to leave a lasting impression on America when they played at the 3-day US Festival, alongside the likes of David Bowie, John (Cougar) Mellencamp and the Pretenders, in

front of an estimated 250,000 people. During the angry, convulsive 'Electric Co', Bono started climbing up a rope ladder and ascended over 100 feet to the top of the stage, still carrying the white flag and microphone in his hand—and then, to the complete horror of the U2 crew, started walking along the top of the canvas, until he felt it ripping beneath him. It was a dangerous, potentially fatal climb, but he made it safely to the ground and, along the way, had ensured that the thousands who were watching below and on TV screens across America would remember the name U2.

Although the band were building their reputation on hard work and solid touring, the music business had now entered the video age. The advent of MTV meant that it had become increasingly possible to clean up the charts without ever even playing a gig. U2's 'New

Right: Bono forging a link between U2 and the rest of the world.

Bono teeters on the edge at the 3-day festival in California in 1983 which attracted an estimated 250,000...

Red Rocks

The location that McGuinness had in mind was Red Rocks, a glorious spot just outside Denver, Colorado, which could accommodate summer crowds of up to 9000 people. As an organization, U2 were only just beginning to make a profit, so McGuinness enlisted the financial help of Island Records and the local promoter. The idea was that U2 would play a show which would be recorded for both a live album and a video, and Steve Lillywhite and Gavin Taylor (of *The Tube*, one of British TV's most prestigious music shows) were flown in to produce the album and direct the video.

Three days before the show, which was scheduled for June 5, it started to rain. Everyone hoped and prayed that the rain would soon let up, but it just got worse. The

Year's Day' video, which mixed shots of the band on a wintery land-scape with bloody war footage, had been repeatedly shown on MTV and, knowing the potential power of that medium, Paul McGuinness was now determined to make a full-length video of U2 live in concert.

...Before plunging head-first into the arms of an enthusiastic and welcoming audience.

Red Rocks: one of the most triumphant shows of U2's career.

promoter and many of the crew thought that U2 should cut their losses and call the whole thing off, but Paul McGuinness was determined that the event would go ahead as planned. He got the local radio station to announce that U2 would play a free concert at a nearby indoor venue the night after Red Rocks for anyone who had to miss the show because of the appallingly bad weather.

In spite of the rain and the lure of the free offer the following night, some 8000 people showed up at Red Rocks for one of the most triumphant shows of U2's career.

Bono, soaked to the skin, clambered across the speaker stacks and out on to a boulder as a magnificent skyline darkened behind him. It was a great moment for the Denver crowd, while those in the UK who saw it on Channel 4's *Midsummer Night Tube Special* were made aware of exactly how much U2 were starting to mean to the rest of the world.

The band returned to Dublin for a triumphant homecoming appearance at Phoenix Park. The bill included Simple Minds, the Eurythmics and Big Country, but most of the 30,000 people who showed up had come to see their local heroes.

It had been a long, hard struggle from the Mount Temple School Gym to here, but U2 weren't about to sit back and feel self-satisfied. They were already aware that the first stage of their journey had ended and that another was about to begin.

Bono pulls U2 back from the brink, and moves upward and onward, taking U2's growing band of admirers with him.

CHAPTER 3

Arrival

In November, 1983, U2 released the live mini-album *Under A Blood Red Sky*. The title was taken from a line in 'New Year's Day' and perfectly described the scenic splendour of Red Rocks, where they had originally recorded the album. However, when the band were actually deciding which tracks to include on the record, they only chose two of the Red Rocks songs ('Gloria' and 'Party Girl') and selected the other five from later shows in Boston and a festival in Germany. They had given the live tapes to Jimmy Iovine (who had worked with people of the stature of John Lennon, Bruce Springsteen and Patti Smith and had become a huge U2 fan on hearing *War*) and he, rather than Steve Lillywhite, was credited as producer.

During the War Tour the band had frequently been

The stylized look of Bono, The Edge, Adam and Larry, an image seemingly at odds with their "normal people" quotes.

The Edge with his wife, Aislinn, in 1988.

accused of being grandiose and overbearing, but the band insisted on including the version of 'Party Girl' that they had recorded at Red Rocks, where The Edge had played a very obvious bum note. The band were convinced that their fans liked them because they walked the line

between triumph and failure and 'Party Girl' was a moment when they had definitely fallen on their faces. Its inclusion on *Under A Blood Red Sky* emphasized the human face of U2. "I think our audience knows that we're actually normal people and we make mistakes and fall over just like everyone else does," Adam would say later. "And I think that's an important thing for people to realize about musicians and music, if they're going to respect it."

Collaboration with Eno

With their live document of the War Tour out of the way now, U2 felt that they could move on to the second phase of their career. Earlier that year, The Edge (who had recently married Aislinn, his girl-friend of the past 6 years) had collaborated with the avant-garde musician Holger Czukay (best known for his work with the German

electronic group Can) on Jah Wobble's *Snake Charmer* EP that had just been a side project to U2, but the whole band were intent on experimenting with U2's sound and understood that they needed a new, innovative producer for their next studio album. The man they all wanted was Brian Eno.

> "I think our audience knows that we're actually normal people and we make mistakes and fall over just like everyone else does."
>
> *Adam*

Best-known for his pioneering synth work in Roxy Music, Eno had gone on to redefine the word "ambient" with a series of albums that had greatly influenced art-based punk bands like Magazine and Wire, and later went on to work with David Bowie and Talking Heads, all of whom were people that U2 greatly admired. Initially, Eno wasn't as keen on the idea of producing U2 as they were, but he agreed to come to Dublin and, after meeting them, was impressed by their honesty and belief in their music and agreed to produce the album.

By this time, Paul McGuinness had renegotiated U2's deal with Island, giving them unprecedented royalty rates and artistic freedom; U2 had also moved their growing organization into a new office suite above the Windmill Lane studio. Rather than making the new album

The Edge moves into the foreground to show off his distinctive guitar sound.

there, U2 were hoping to create a more impressionistic sound by recording on a portable desk in Slane Castle (the site of their show with Thin Lizzy in 1981), and shut themselves away with Brian Eno and his engineer, Daniel Lanois.

The Unforgettable Fire

The title of *The Unforgettable Fire* was inspired by a collection of gruesomely graphic paintings and drawings by the survivors of Hiroshima and Nagasaki which had been exhibited at the Peace Museum in Chicago, a centre devoted to the life of Martin Luther King and the promotion of non-violence through the arts. However, although the threat of nuclear holocaust hangs over *The Unforgettable Fire* (as, indeed, it had with *War*), the title also refers to the spiritual fire that burned within people like Martin Luther King and Elvis Presley (who between them directly inspired three of the album's ten tracks).

The recording of *The Unforgettable Fire* was not without its difficulties: the session started at Slane Castle in May before moving to Windmill Lane in June, threatening to overrun its July deadline, but eventually winding up on schedule. However, the band learned a great deal about sound and also their own capabilities. Barry Devlin (who had produced their second demo back in 1978) made a short documentary for an RTE TV special called *The Making of the Unforgettable Fire*, which gives a valuable and revealing insight into the band's creative process.

Talks with Dylan

While Eno was wrapping up the album, Bono returned to Slane Castle to watch Bob Dylan play in front of 40,000 people. Before Dylan went on stage, Bono conducted an interview with him for *Hot Press*. During its course, Bono was surprised to hear him talk

Bono, the man untouched by the musical tradition of his own country, changing the face of Irish music

Bono and Adam appearing on MTV in 1984.

Wolf. His curiosity sparked, Bono told Dylan, "I'd like to know more about roots music. I'm hungry for a past."

Dylan showed his respect for Bono when he invited him on stage to sing 'Leopardskin Pillbox Hat'. Bono didn't know the words, but Dylan generously asked him back for an encore of 'Blowin' In The Wind'. Unfortunately, by the time Bono got the microphone Dylan had already sung the only verses that he knew. Undaunted, he did one of his usual improvisations and made up a verse of his own, changing the tune in the process. Bob didn't seem to mind, but some of Dylan's fans were less than impressed by his impromptu contribution.

Celtic roots

Although Bono had told Dylan that he had never plugged into any particular musical roots or heritage, this assertion isn't borne out by the music written for U2. His rebellion

about the Clancy Brothers and Brendan Behan and of the central influence that Irish folk music had had on his work. Bono confessed that he had never plugged into the Irish tradition and told Dylan that he envied him because U2's music, by contrast, seemed to be "caught in space". Dylan advised him to "reach back", pointing him in the direction of the McPeakes and later (when Van Morrison had also joined in the conversation) talking about great American bluesmen such as Robert Johnson, Hank Williams, Muddy Waters and Howlin'

"I'd like to know more about roots music. I'm hungry for a past."

Bono

against Irish culture and learning Gaelic, could not cut off his Irish roots or prevent their influence on U2's songs. They were apparent in 'An Cat Dubh' (on *Boy*), the haunt-ing 'Tomorrow' (on *October*) and now in the easy spontaneity of *The Unforgettable Fire*, especially in the new album's opening track, appro-priately entitled 'A Sort of

Bono in characteristic performing pose, at the edge of the stage, reaching out to the audience.

"Our choice: band of the Eighties"

Rolling Stone

Homecoming', a stirring evocation of the wild, Celtic landscape.

Meanwhile, the band was making its influence on the Irish music business felt. The four of them knew how difficult it had been for them to get a break or even advice as a young band 4 years ago and now they were keen to help others in the same situation, both by expanding the recording facilities at Windmill Lane and by setting up their own label, Mother

Bono in triumphant mood at Milton Keynes Bowl in June 1985, the band's only British date that year.

Records. The first single to appear on Mother (in July 1984) was 'Coming Thru' by the Celtic rock group In Tua Nua, whose uilleann piper Vinnie Kilduff and violinist Steve Wickham had respectively recorded and toured with U2 on their *October* and *War* albums, and had once featured a 14-year-old vocalist called Sinead O'Connor.

The Unforgettable Fire hits the top

'Pride (In The Name Of Love)' provided a great taster for *The Unforgettable Fire* when it was released in September, 1984. A moving tribute to the American Civil Rights leader Dr Martin Luther King wasn't exactly the usual chart fodder but this was a classic pop song and it gave U2 their first UK Top 5 hit, reaching Number 33 in the US. Although *The Unforgettable Fire* shot straight into the UK Number 1 spot a month later, it surprised a lot of U2 fans by placing the emphasis unequivocally on emotion and ambience rather than energy and histrionics.

The album had two truly great songs in 'Pride' and the cinematic 'Bad' which followed a friend through the desperate, desolate world of smack addiction. But as well as writing crafted songs, Eno had helped U2 to rediscover their inner spirit and spontaneity. The latter showed in the flawed but heartfelt 'Elvis Presley And America', a stream of consciousness that was recorded in a matter of a few minutes.

Back on the road again

U2 spent the next 6 months on the road: Australia, New Zealand, Europe and 4 months in the United States. In March they appeared on the cover of *Rolling Stone* with the accolade, "Our choice: band of the Eighties". In April they played to a capacity crowd at New York's Madison Square Gardens (the show had sold out in an hour). By this time they were comfortable with the songs from *The Unforgettable Fire* and Bono was now throwing snatches of the Rolling Stones' 'Ruby Tuesday' and Lou Reed's 'I'm Waiting For The Man' into 'Bad'.

The band's only British date of the year was at Milton Keynes Bowl on June 22. A week later they played in front of 55,000 people at Dublin's Croke Park. It was their biggest Irish show ever, and was

Adam playing at the Milton Keynes Bowl in June 1985.

The Edge setting the mood at New York's Madison Square Gardens.

aimed to bring further relief to the famine victims of Ethiopia by organizing Live Aid, a global charity event that would be broadcast from two stadia (London's Wembley and Philadelphia's JFK) to 1½ billion people around the world.

U2 were one of the 22 acts who were scheduled for the Wembley stage. They were given a 5 o'clock slot, with 15 minutes to perform 'Sunday Bloody Sunday', 'Bad' and 'Pride (In The Name Of Love)'. They began with 'Sunday Bloody Sunday' then bled into 'Bad'. As he sang the words of that desolate song, Bono was more desperate to commune with the 72,000 people in the crowd than he had ever been before. He seemed to have forgotten about the 15 minutes only rule as he sang the now familiar snatches of other songs: 'Satellite Of Love' followed by 'Ruby Tuesday' and 'Sympathy For The Devil' while he roamed the stage, looking out to the crowd, wanting to include them

prefixed by a dual exhibition of the original "Unforgettable Fire" and "Martin Luther King—Peacemaker" at Dublin's Grapevine Arts Centre, which amplified the atrocity of nuclear warfare and the struggle of Martin Luther King.

Live Aid
The previous November, Bono and Adam had taken part in Bob Geldof's Band Aid charity single, 'Do They Know It's Christmas?', which had gone on to sell 3½ million copies. Inspired by that, Geldof

Live Aid, the ground-breaking get-together of stars to raise money for the starving in Ethiopia, with Bono, Bob Geldof and Midge Ure (on the left).

too. He reached the edge of the stage, then noticed a girl at the front; she signalled to him, he moved towards her, then, with the eyes of the world upon him, he jumped down into the no-man's land between the stage and the security barriers, ran to the girl and hugged her as though he were embracing the whole world. This was the moment that summed up the spirit of Live Aid, the moment that no one watching would ever forget.

Far from feeling elated, however, Bono felt he had blown it, shot U2 in the head in front of the whole world. Back in Ireland, he just drove around for days, unable to communicate with anyone. He kept thinking about the millions dying of starvation and wondered what he was doing performing in something as banal as a rock 'n' roll band.

As he travelled around the Irish countryside, he met a sculptor, an older man who knew very little about music. Ironically, the man was working on a piece which he called "The Leap", an attempt to reproduce the spirit of Live Aid through an image that U2 had themselves provided for him. After that, Bono went back home and started to believe people when they said that the part of Live Aid that they remembered best was Bono leaping into the crowd and embracing the girl.

After Live Aid, Bono and his wife, Alison, spent 5 (unpublicized) weeks in Ethiopia, working as volunteers for World Vision on an educational relief project, where they attempted to educate people about health and hygiene through a series of songs and short plays.

Bono and Adam on stage during the Live Aid concert. Bono was so elated by the occasion that U2 overran their 15-minute slot.

Sun City

On his return to Dublin, Bono learned about a massive anti-apartheid project that was being organized by Little Steven (Steven Van Zandt, also known as Miami Steve, the guitarist in Bruce Springsteen's E Street Band). Little Steven had already lined up a series of names for the *Sun City: Artists Against Apartheid* LP, including Bob Dylan, Lou Reed, Pete Townshend, Bruce Springsteen and Peter Wolf (the singer in the J. Geils Band who had let the struggling post-*October* U2 support them back in 1982). He wanted Bono to add vocals and a spoken message to the album, and to take part in the video that they were about to start shooting.

Bono flew to New York, taking with him a cassette that he had recorded of the young Dublin shop assistants who had been sacked

Bono gives an impromptu guitar lesson to a bemused fan.

from Dunnes store in the city centre for refusing to handle South African products. The assistants were picketing the shop, action which had put them at the centre of a political row in Ireland. On his arrival in New York, Bono (still jetlagged from his trip to Ethiopia) was reintroduced to Peter Wolf and Bruce Springsteen, and had the first of many meetings with Lou Reed, whose songs were frequently integrated into U2's sets.

Bono lines up with Little Steven (right) for *Artists Against Apartheid*.

Recording with Keith

Later that evening, Peter Wolf took him to the New York studio where the Rolling Stones were recording their *Dirty Work* LP with Steve Lillywhite. Bono ended up staying out half the night with Keith Richards, Mick Jagger and Peter Wolf, listening to Keith bash out blues, country and early rock 'n' roll songs on the piano and guitar. Bono admitted later that he was "very down" about his inability to come up with songs of his own, and was painfully aware that he didn't have the grasp on the past urged on him by Dylan.

Dejected, Bono trooped back to his hotel room, got out his guitar and wrote two songs, 'Silver And Gold' and 'This I've Got To Stop', in a couple of hours. Set in a South African prison cell, 'Silver And Gold' was Bono's first attempt at the blues, and he asked Keith Richards to record it with him—which he did, along with Ronnie Wood. The song

was finished just in time to make it on to the *Sun City* album.

Looking for the roots

Back home again, Bono got together with Maire Ni Bhraonain (the singer in Clannad, one of his favourite Irish groups) to record a single called 'In A Lifetime'. Bono had fallen in love with the Donegal woman's voice on hearing her sing

Bono sees double with Pete Townshend at the Rock 'n' Roll Hall of Fame induction ceremony.

the haunting 'Theme From Harry's Game', which was credited with being the first Gaelic record to reach the UK Top 5 back in 1982 and was regularly used by U2 as an atmospheric ending to their live set. As well as contributing his vocal to

'In A Lifetime', Bono went to Clannad's home base of Gweedore to make a promo video and spoke of the importance of tradition and humanity in music.

Ever since his meeting at Slane with Bob Dylan the year before, Bono had become increasingly preoccupied with discovering the roots of popular music. He immersed himself in a huge collection of blues records, some recommended by Dylan, others by Robbie Robertson (former singer in the Band) and the rest borrowed from a friend. Meanwhile, The Edge (inspired by the band's work with Eno) had been busy composing a film soundtrack, demo-ing it with Larry and trying to find a director who might be able to use it, while Larry and Adam had become increasingly involved in the running of Mother Records.

Yet it wasn't just Bono who was delving into the past. Through their travels in America and sporadic

In the mid Eighties, Bono became increasingly preoccupied with the quest for his musical roots.

63

Larry and Adam performing before their home crowd at the Self-Aid benefit concert in Dublin in May 1986. U2 topped the bill of 27 acts which included such Irish musical alumni as Clannad, Elvis Costello, the Boomtown Rats and Van Morrison.

contact with older musicians like Robbie Robertson, all four members of U2 were now aware of the rich musical legacy that they had walked away from in 1976 when they were first exposed to punk. In addition to the blues, Larry had become more and more of a country and western fan and was anxious for U2 to sit down and write some straightforward songs. In the past, U2 had unwittingly written a series of great songs in 'I Will Follow', 'New Year's Day' and (more knowingly) in 'Pride (In The Name Of Love)', but now they were ready to make an album that would marry the evocative atmospherics of *The Unforgettable Fire* to simple, well-structured songs. The four of them reconvened in Larry's bedroom towards the end of 1985 and, with a small amp, a cassette recorder and a pile of the drummer's country and western records, began to plot the course that would lead to the recording of their visionary album, *The Joshua Tree*.

Self-Aid

Apart from a one-off RTE TV appearance and a low-key gig in Ireland, U2 had kept well out of the public eye since Live Aid. They made a brief comeback in May 1986 when they appeared at the Irish

Unemployment Benefit, Self-Aid, in front of 30,000 people in their home town's Royal Dublin Showground. Although the line-up of 27 acts also included Van Morrison, Christy Moore, the Boomtown Rats, Elvis Costello, Clannad and Cactus World News (who had released a Bono-produced single on Mother the previous

Bono presenting a new face at the Self-Aid concert, uncharacteristically shying away from reporters.

summer), it was a photograph of U2 that appeared on the cover of *In Dublin* magazine under the heading "The Great Self-Aid Farce, Rock Against The People". However, the author of the cover article, Eamonn McCann, wasn't personally attacking U2 as much as criticizing the government for off-loading responsibility for the unemployed on to a bunch of generous-spirited post-Live Aid rock bands.

Headlining the show, U2 took everyone by surprise when they opened their set with a rollicking great version of Eddie Cochran's 'C'mon Everybody', with Bono playing opposite The Edge on a beautiful black acoustic guitar. In among the band's expected standards like 'Pride' and 'Sunday Bloody Sunday', were their versions of Bob Dylan's 'Maggie's Farm' and John Lennon's

The Edge on stage during the Conspiracy of Hope Tour in June 1986, a series of benefits for Amnesty.

Bono with his hero, Lou Reed, who turned out for the final benefit given for Amnesty in New York.

Conspiracy of Hope

The following month, U2 interrupted the preparations for their next album by flying to the States for the Amnesty International Conspiracy of Hope Tour. U2 had originally been asked to take part in some kind of benefit to celebrate Amnesty's twenty-fifth birthday, but the idea eventually escalated into a six-city tour that featured the likes of Sting, Lou Reed, Peter Gabriel, the Neville Brothers and Bryan Adams. It not only helped to raise $3 million (£2 million) but also doubled the organization's membership in America.

The climax of the tour was a performance at the New York Giants' Stadium in front of 53,000 people. On this occasion U2 were joined on stage by Little Steven and Lou Reed for a triumphant blast of

'Cold Turkey', comments on Ireland's unemployment and smack problems. These songs bled into the eerie, pre-taped sound of bomber planes and air strikes. "Chernobyl's got me on the run," Bono cried out to the audience—referring to the world's worst nuclear accident which had occurred near Kiev, in the USSR, just 3 weeks before—as he shone a huge spotlight directly into the faces in the crowd. 'Bad' closed the set, with the whole crowd singing along to the final refrain of 'Walk On The Wild Side'.

Sting and Bono during the Conspiracy of Hope Tour.

'Sun City' and, repeating the effect they had had at Self-Aid, Dylan's 'Maggie's Farm'. The Police had to follow the band on stage to make their farewell appearance, but they acknowledged how difficult it had been when they handed their instruments to U2 for the final number. Every band has its day, Sting reasoned at the time, and he was certain that it was going to be U2's turn next.

The death of Greg Carroll

Within days of their return to Dublin, U2 were thrown into despair when Bono's personal assistant and close

The finale of the Conspiracy of Hope Tour at the New York Giants' Stadium in 1986. U2 interrupted preparations for their next album in order to participate in the six-city tour.

friend Greg Carroll was killed in a motorbike accident. His body was flown back to New Zealand where he had first met U2 during The Unforgettable Fire Tour.

Bono and Larry flew to Auckland for his funeral and the singer later eulogized his memory in 'One Tree Hill', a song which was named after the tallest of the volcanic mounds that overlook Auckland's harbour and which also happened to be the name of the town where the band had first met Carroll. Because he was a Maori, Carroll was buried in his tribal homeland, after a wake that lasted for 3 days and nights. Shocked and deeply saddened, Bono and Larry returned to Dublin to finish work on the album that they would dedicate to his memory.

CHAPTER 4

The biggest band in the world

Throughout 1986 it had been common knowledge that U2 would again be working with the Brian Eno/Daniel Lanois partnership that had produced *The Unforgettable Fire*, so when The Edge released his *Captive* film score in September there was a great deal of speculation as to whether or not this spacy, Eno-esque record was indicative of U2's next step. The Edge refused to give too much away, but promised that the new record would be U2's "best album to date".

When *The Joshua Tree* finally arrived in March 1987, it proved The Edge to be as good as his word. The new record was acknowledged to be one of the finest records of the decade. Produced by Eno/Lanois (with three remixes by Steve Lillywhite), the vague landscapes traversed in *The Unforgettable Fire* had now been harnessed to fully formed songs.

U2 fans demonstrate their approval of *The Joshua Tree*—record and tour—in 1987.

An American album

The Joshua Tree was frequently described as "an American album", and in many ways it was: U2 seemed both attracted to it ('In God's Country') and repelled by it (the stunning 'Bullet The Blue Sky'). The record took its title from a small town in Death Valley, California, where the country singer Gram Parsons was cremated, and the gatefold cover (photographed by Anton Corbijn) showed the band on the edge of the desert.

The sense of emptiness that those vast desert plains conjured up was reflected in the spiritual yearning of the epic 'With Or Without You', 'I Still Haven't Found What I'm Looking For' and 'Where The Streets Have No Name' (all three songs would become US and UK Top 10 singles, and the first would go on to sell 4 million worldwide). Yet although they soared like great gospel songs they were filled with restlessness and confusion, while

tracks like 'Running To Stand Still' (which covered the same smacked-out streets as 'Bad') and 'Exit' resonated with a darkness previously absent from the band's work.

U2 weren't just interested in traversing national or spiritual borders—their songs also included social, political and sexual concerns. 'Bullet The Blue Sky' was

Larry Mullen comes of age.

a fierce attack on the US presence in El Salvador; 'Mothers of the Disappeared' dealt with abduction and torture in South America; 'Red Hill Mining Town' examined the breakdown of the relationship between a miner and his wife during

Larry on stage during *The Joshua Tree* tour.

the 1984–5 British Miners' Strike; and in 'Exit', a man broken by his experiences is pushed into the abyss of madness. Musically, U2 had truly come of age: Larry shuffling on his snare or banging away with military precision, The Edge's guitar switching from the slightest shivers of touch to thundering great slabs of heavy metal, and

Adam's bass lines throbbing beneath it all like a human heart; lyrically, they were now painting the whole canvas rather than throwing some colour on and watching it run, and Bono's voice had never sounded so good.

Reaching in all directions

The week before *The Joshua Tree* was due to hit the streets in March 1987, U2 appeared on RTE's *Late Late Show* in Dublin to take part in the Dubliners' twenty-fifth birthday celebrations. Christy Moore, the Pogues, the Fureys and Stockton's Wing had all turned up to sing a song that the Dubliners had either written or popularized. U2 chose Peggy Seeger's 'Springhill Mining Disaster', which Bono sang with the kind of passion and intensity reminiscent of the Dubliners' late lead singer, Luke Kelly.

U2 were no longer "in space somewhere", but exploring areas

Adam enjoys a rare break while on tour.

that Bob Dylan had advised Bono to "reach back" for. The band proved they were capable of reaching in many different directions at a pre-*Joshua Tree* gig at Belfast's King's Hall; former In Tua Nua singer Sinead O'Connor, who had recently co-written and sung a track on The Edge's *Captive* LP, was in support. Their set included Curtis Mayfield's 'People Get Ready', Neil Young's 'Southern Man' and the Undertones' 'Teenage Kicks'.

When *The Joshua Tree* finally went on sale, London's Tower Records were so aware of public demand that they put it on sale at midnight, and had a thousand people (including Elvis Costello) queueing round Piccadilly. The album went straight to the top of the British charts by selling a quarter of a million in the first week.

Bono, unaware that he is causing a "civil disturbance" by making a video on the roof of an LA store.

Back in the USA

Few people would have predicted that *The Joshua Tree* and its first two singles, 'With Or Without You' and 'I Still Haven't Found What I'm Looking For', were all destined for the Number 1 spot in America. U2 began their world tour in the

"Rock's hottest ticket"
Time magazine

country that had inspired much of *The Joshua Tree* at the beginning of April, and by the end of the month they had been elevated to the ranks of the Beatles and the Who when they became the third-ever rock band to appear on the cover of *Time* magazine.

The *Time* article described them as "Rock's hottest ticket". During the band's 5-night stint at the Los Angeles Sports Arena, the likes of Mickey Rourke, Harry Dean Stanton, Madonna and Sean Penn turned up for their shows and Bob Dylan joined them on stage for versions of 'Knockin' On Heaven's Door' and 'I Shall Be Released'. Suddenly, U2 were a household name in America and everything they did seemed to be of monumental significance. The police even stopped them from making a video on the roof of a Los Angeles

Bono and the law, backed by the bright neon of Las Vegas.

"After *The Joshua Tree* I really feel we can do whatever we want to. I don't feel that there's any area of music that we can't get involved in."

The Edge

Bono and Adam, after the singer had broken his arm on the second leg of The Joshua Tree Tour.

store on the grounds that they were likely to cause a civil disturbance.

The hysteria grows

After 6 weeks in the States the tour continued in Europe, taking in both Wembley Arena and Stadium in

London and 2 days at Dublin's Croke Park, supported by various friends like Lou Reed, the Pretenders, UB40, BAD, Lone Justice and the Pogues. The 2½-hour shows on the tour were spectacular—particularly during 'Bullet The Blue Sky', where, reproducing the same effect that he had first employed at Self-Aid, Bono would shine a spotlight into the crowd while The Edge's blistering guitar solos reflected the chaos and devastation of the song. But the show had much lighter moments,

with U2 continuing to pay homage to rock 'n' roll's rich past by throwing in snatches of Eddie Cochran's 'C'mon Everybody', Joy Division's 'Love Will Tear Us Apart', the Doors' 'Break On Through', the Beatles' 'Help' and Johnny Cash's 'Folsom Prison Blues'.

As U2 returned to the States at the end of the summer, the scale of the venues and the attendant hysteria grew. By the end of the year, *The Joshua Tree* had sold an astonishing 12 million worldwide. "After *The Joshua Tree* I really feel we can do whatever we want to," said The Edge as the year went on. "I don't feel that there's any area of music that we can't get involved in."

After U2's Los Angeles show, Bono sat up half the night writing a song with Bob Dylan and T-Bone Burnett. He started to compose a whole series of songs for musicians

U2 on stage in Los Angeles.

he admired: for the blues legend B. B. King he wrote 'When Love Comes To Town' and 'Lucille' (the latter a country song about B.B.'s guitar) and for Roy Orbison 'She's A Mystery To Me'—a song which was inspired by Orbison's performance of 'In Dreams' in the David Lynch movie *Blue Velvet*, and which had a dark beauty that set it apart from most of the songs that Bono had previously written.

The darker side

Although U2 had hinted at a new, darker side on 'Bad' (from *The Unforgettable Fire*), it wasn't until *The Joshua Tree* that they had really begun to explore it. The songs on the B side of 'With Or Without You', for example, covered the same kind of dark sexual terrain as 'She's A Mystery To Me';

U2 live out their policy of being accessible to their fans during the US tour at the end of 1987.

'Luminous Times (Hold Onto Love)' was vague and sombre but lyrically direct, while 'Walk To The Water' dealt with sexual obsession of a different kind. Over the past year, Bono's lyrics had been increasingly informed by American writers like Truman Capote, Charles Bukowski, Raymond Carver and Norman Mailer (whose *The Executioner's Song* had directly influenced 'Exit'). Inspirational, too, were the violence and spiritual malaise explored by Flannery O'Connor in her books about the Deep South. With these trans-Atlantic voices combining with those of Irish writers such as Seamus Heaney, Patrick Kavanagh

The Edge remains unmoved by Bono's serenading.

and Brendan Behan, Bono was now writing the kind of lyrics that would do full justice to the rich, vast sweep of U2's music.

The genesis of Rattle And Hum

During The Joshua Tree Tour, there seemed to be many new directions that U2 could move in. The band opted for a full-scale excavation of blues, gospel and country—musical genres that would be brought to life on the album and film that became Rattle And Hum.

Given that the Under A Blood Red Sky video was 4 years old and way out of step with what U2 were doing now, Paul McGuinness wanted to make a full-length feature film of U2 on the road. This idea developed as The Joshua Tree Tour progressed. The band had originally

The four members of U2 surround some of the stars of A Very Special Christmas in 1987.

been interested in working with director Jonathan Demme (largely because of his work on Talking Heads' Stop Making Sense concert movie), but in May they met and were greatly impressed by Phil Joanou, a 26-year-old film graduate who had done some minor work with Steven Spielberg.

During the summer U2 and Joanou developed their plans for Rattle And Hum. They decided to include plenty of documentary footage but very little in the way of soul-baring interviews—the music and the action would speak for them. Joanou accompanied the band on the second leg of The Joshua Tree Tour, shooting for 3½ months and eventually amassing 250 hours of film.

Visiting Sun Studio

One of the highlights of both the soundtrack and the movie Rattle And Hum and, indeed, of U2's career, was their visit to the Sun

Studio in Memphis. Surrounded by huge portraits of Elvis Presley, Carl Perkins, Jerry Lee Lewis and Johnny Cash, U2 felt as they were stepping into the heart of rock 'n' roll. The session was recorded by "Cowboy" Jack Clement, who had produced some of the greatest names in rock 'n' roll (Lewis, Cash, Roy Orbison and Charlie Rich) and who had written the Johnny Cash hits 'Ballad Of A Teenage Queen' and 'Guess Things Happen That Way'. Clement was greatly valued by U2, partly because he kept them entertained with good humour and neat tricks (like balancing bottles on his head) and also because he had a wealth of stories about the legends who had previously recorded at Sun.

They were joined in the studio by B. B. King (who was happy to sing 'When Love Comes To Town', the song that Bono had written for him), Bob Dylan (who sang 'Love Rescue Me') and the Memphis Horns (who

Betty and Alton Dalton playing country and western in America.

played on 'Angel Of Harlem'); all three songs would later show up on the *Rattle And Hum* soundtrack.

In addition to recording songs for *Rattle And Hum*, Jimmy Iovine (who would take the production credit for *Rattle And Hum*) asked the band to appear alongside Madonna, Bruce Springsteen, Run DMC and a host of other big names on the Special Olympics charity album, *A Very Special Christmas*, for which they did a great version of Phil Spector's 'Christmas (Baby Please Come Home)'. They also

"Rock 'n' Roll Stops the Traffic."

Bono – graffiti

'sang Jesus Christ' on the Woody Guthrie album *A Vision Shared*, and played on one of the tracks on their old friend Robbie Robertson's comeback album.

The Dalton Brothers

Throughout 1987, U2 were immersing themselves deeper and deeper in all forms of roots and rock 'n' roll; of all of them, it was Larry who was the keenest country fan (although Bono had been blown away when he first discovered Willie Nelson). Towards the end of the year, the group amused themselves by forming their own country band,

the Dalton Brothers. The joke began when one of their support bands, Los Lobos, missed their flight to a concert in October. U2 donned wigs and suitable attire (in Adam's case a dress), adopted the stage names of Alton (Bono), Luke (The Edge), Duke (Larry) and Betty (Adam) and opened their own show. "We have two kinds of music here for you—country and western,"

Alton Dalton told the bemused crowd before the Daltons shambled their way through several versions of Bono's country song, 'Lucille', and had a storming great go at Hank Williams's 'Lost Highway'. However, the few crowds who were treated to this spectacle were so keyed up to see U2 that they did not give the Daltons a second thought, oblivious to the fact that they were letting a small chunk of rock history pass them quietly by.

> "We don't write a song like 'Bullet The Blue Sky' because we think Reagan will hear it and move out of Nicaragua. People would be very naive to think that one band could change the tide politically."
>
> *The Edge*

From the left: Adam, Larry, Bono and The Edge on the set of the 'Desire' video.

Rock 'n' roll stops the traffic

By this time, though, everything that U2 did had taken on such monumental significance that no one could imagine them doing some-

thing "just for a laugh". For instance, when they played a free lunchtime show in San Francisco's city centre (which they laughingly referred to as a Save the Yuppies Concert) and Bono sprayed "Rock 'n' Roll Stops the Traffic" over a nearby statue, it became a national scandal. Everyone was looking for the political significance and deep meaning invested in his slogan (and some were even wondering if U2 were seriously pro-yuppies). Back home in Britain, the band had been the subject of a World In Action UK TV special which portrayed them as the serious, highly political spokesmen of rock. "We don't write a song like 'Bullet The Blue Sky' because we think Reagan will hear it and move out of Nicaragua," stated The Edge. "People would be very naive to think that one band could change the tide politically."

Rather than trying to change anything, U2 were intent on shaking off the shackles of responsibility by simply exploring rock 'n' roll. Although they won Grammy Awards for Album of the Year and Best

Happiness is...receiving a Grammy award.

Rock Performance, U2 spent half of 1988 in LA's A&M studio recording and mixing the 17 tracks that would appear on the *Rattle And Hum* album. Meanwhile, Phil Joanou spent 9 months whittling The Joshua Tree Tour footage down to 1 hour 39 minutes.

Rattle And Hum goes twice platinum

Rattle And Hum was preceded, in September 1988, by 'Desire', a truly great rock 'n' roll single that gave U2 their first UK Number 1 (it reached Number 3 in the US). The double album—which took its title

The Edge arriving at the Dublin premiere of *Rattle And Hum*, the movie.

from a line in 'Bullet The Blue Sky'—followed a month later, and went twice platinum in the UK before it was even released. Opening with a killer live cut of the Beatles' 'Helter Skelter', *Rattle And Hum* was a massive toast to U2's heroes, living and dead: Bob Dylan and B. B. King

in the Sun session; Jimi Hendrix performing a 43-second snatch of 'The Star Spangled Banner'; Dylan again on 'All Along The Watch Tower' (from the San Francisco concert); and tributes to John Lennon (in 'God Part II', a righteous putdown of Elvis/Lennon biographer Albert Goldman) and Billie Holiday (in 'Angel Of Harlem'). There were brilliant live versions of 'Bullet The Blue Sky', 'Pride' and 'Silver And Gold' and a handful of other new studio tracks—notably 'Hawkmoon 269' with Dylan on keyboards, 'All I Want Is You' and 'Van Diemen's Land' (about an Irish poet who was arrested by the British government and exiled to Australia, and unusual in that the lyrics were written and sung by The Edge).

Rattle And Hum, the movie

The *Rattle And Hum* movie was released at the same time

(along with an accompanying book of the same name, designed by Steve Averill). Opening in black and white, changing to colour and then reverting to monochrome, *Rattle And Hum* caught U2 in a series of locations from Joanou's first night's shooting in disastrous conditions in Arizona to a church with a gospel choir in Harlem, Elvis's grave at Graceland, Sun Studio and Dublin's

> "I'm sick and tired of Irish Americans coming up to me and talking about the glory of the revolution. Fuck the revolution."
>
> *Bono*

cover of the Beatles' 'Helter Skelter' (a song which, like 'Help', had fascinated Bono, because the Beatles had written the songs at the height of their fame).

The end of 'Sunday Bloody Sunday'?

Although the movie included Bono's spray-painting antics in San Francisco, this was small change

desolate docklands. *Rattle And Hum* was never meant to highlight the personalities in U2—it was always meant to be about the music, and most of the film is taken up with imaginative live footage.

Although *Rattle And Hum* the album was frequently referred to as a soundtrack, the real *Rattle And Hum* soundtrack differs from the album both in terms of versions and actual songs. The movie included a handful of tracks that weren't on the album, but both the movie and the album began with U2's stunning

U2 fans gather for a glimpse of the *Rattle And Hum* stars.

Bono, an impassioned singer, puts his all into the vocals.

when compared to his passionate introduction to *Rattle And Hum*, played to an American audience on the night that 13 people were massacred by an IRA bomb in Enniskillen. "I'm sick and tired of Irish Americans coming up to me and talking about the glory of the revolution. Fuck the revolution," he spat. U2 had clearly come a long way since the days when Bono would bluster around, singing 'Sunday Bloody Sunday' with his white flag. "I'm not sure that we'll ever play that song again," he said on BBC's Radio 1. "I've just about had it up to here with 'Sunday Bloody Sunday' and the weight it carries."

Accused of arrogance

Although *Rattle And Hum* reached Number 1 in the charts in both Britain and America, the inevitable

Bono bears up to the burden of being a living legend.

"If you look at the cover of *The Joshua Tree*, you see four very unhappy men...What nobody realizes is that it was −20 out there. We were freezing. Put any bastard out there and see if he's happy." *Larry*

backlash had already begun. *Rattle And Hum* was dissected for hidden meanings and, when none was apparent, was widely interpreted as an arrogant attempt on U2's part to elevate themselves to the pantheon of greats in the rock 'n' roll hall of fame, alongside the Beatles, Hendrix and Dylan.

The band appeared to be genuinely horrified that there was so much room for misinterpretation: they had intended *Rattle And Hum* to be a fans' tribute to the musicians who were inspirational to them, complete with visuals, because, as Bono said, "There are people out there who probably don't even know who B. B. King is." (He would be proved right later when B. B. King, enjoying a massively increased post-U2 fan base, said that he'd never be able to thank U2 enough for freezing his picture on the *Rattle And Hum* screen so that people would know him). Yet the *Rattle And Hum* movie was seen as

further irrefutable proof of U2's arrogance and they found themselves accused, among other things, of assuming a "smothering self-importance".

Four dour men

One major criticism of *Rattle And Hum* was that U2 didn't give anything of themselves away, while the black and white footage reinforced the image of U2 as the four austere men on the cover of *The Joshua Tree*. "If you look at the cover of *The Joshua Tree*," said Larry, "you see four very unhappy men. Now, you may ask, why? A lot of people will say, 'They're feeling guilty, they've got the weight of the world on their shoulders. They've been involved in the Save the Whale campaign, and they're very unhappy about it.' What nobody realizes is that it was –20 out there.

Bono on stage with "the Mayor of Love Town", B. B. King.

We were freezing. Put any bastard out there and see if he's happy."

U2 had invested $5 million (£3.3 million) of their own money in the *Rattle And Hum* movie, but once the hardcore fans had seen it the attendance dropped off and it was out of America's main movie theatres by Christmas. Similarly, although the next three *Rattle And Hum* singles ('Angel Of Harlem', 'When Love Comes To Town' and 'All I Want Is You') would all hit the UK Top 10 during the first half of 1989, only one of them made it into *Billboard*'s Top 60. America, it seemed, had overdosed on U2.

Dreaming it all up again

For their part U2 had certainly had enough of the exposure, and they kept a low profile for most of 1989. They emerged in September to begin the 4-month Love Town Tour, which began in Australia, New Zealand and Japan

> ## "We have to go away and just dream it all up again."
>
> ## *Bono*

and finished in Europe (significantly leaving America out). Their set list was built around the *Rattle And Hum* album, with special guest B. B. "the Mayor of Love Town" King and his mini-orchestra joining them on stage every night for a three-song medley of 'Angel Of Harlem', 'Love Rescue Me' and 'When Love Comes To Town'. The tour ended with 4 nights at Dublin's Point Depot and the final night—which happened to be New Year's Eve—was broadcast to a European radio audience of an estimated 500 million.

It was a great finale, but when Bono sang about needing new dreams tonight during 'In God's Country', he meant it. As the band left the stage on the last night of the 1980s, Bono told them: "We have to go away and just dream it all up again." The Love Town Tour had closed the final chapter of U2's *The Joshua Tree/Rattle And Hum* period, just as *Under A Blood Red Sky* had been the last word on the *War* era 5 years before.

Bono in search of a new dream for the Nineties.

CHAPTER 5

The new dream

When Bono said that the band had to "go away", he immediately sparked rumours of a U2 split. What he actually meant was that the four of them would take a long break in order to regenerate their creative powers. Larry soon found an outlet for his when he produced the single 'Put 'Em Under Pressure' for Ireland's World Cup soccer squad, which featured them and their manager Jack Charlton, the piper Davey Spillane and Maire from Clannad.

A few months later, Bono appeared on British TV's *South Bank Show* in a documentary (made by Bob Geldof's TV production company) called "Cool, Clear Crystal Streams". Bono talked about songwriting and what it means to be an Irish songwriter. The programme also featured Van Morrison, Sinead O'Connor, Christy Moore, Shane MacGowan, Hot House Flowers and Clannad, and threw in a series of great Irish writers and lyricists like Sean O'Casey, James Joyce and Patrick Kavanagh. If U2's exploration of American blues, gospel, folk and country had done anything, it was to show them

Bono regenerated his creative powers and eventually re-emerged as "the Fly".

that their own roots were the most valuable source of inspiration of all. "I never knew I was Irish until I went to America," Bono frequently told journalists.

Bringing it all back home

Mirroring U2's discovery was *Bringing it All Back Home* (a five-part Irish TV series and also a book), which traced the return journey that Irish traditional music has made to America and further-flung parts of the world. In addition to Bono singing a song he had written a couple of years earlier called 'Wild Irish Rose', the series featured the likes of Christy Moore, the Pogues, Hothouse Flowers (a band who had released their first single on U2's Mother label in 1987 and were now enjoying worldwide success), the Everly Brothers, Emmylou Harris and, now resident in Dublin, Elvis Costello and the Waterboys.

The Dublin of 1990 was a very different city (at least as far as the music industry was concerned) from the one that U2 had struggled out of a decade earlier. Mother Records had provided many young bands with access to the kind of recording facilities and producers that they would only otherwise have

U2 in the Nineties, on the Zoo TV Tour.

been able to obtain if they had signed a major deal. U2 had also focused the attention of the music industry on Ireland: A&R men the world over were coming to Dublin to search for "the next U2".

Adam tries to ignore the devil on his left-hand shoulder.

Inspiration in Berlin

In the summer of 1990, however, U2 flew to Berlin to look for inspiration for their next album. They decked out their cars with huge sound systems and drove round the city blasting their heads off with a mixture of rap, reggae and dance music. They decided that Berlin would be the ideal place to record the new album, particularly since the Berlin Wall was in the process of being dismantled brick by brick: Germany's state of flux would reflect the changes they felt in themselves.

U2 arrived in Berlin at the beginning of October, just in time to celebrate Liberation and Unification Day. They had already chosen German film director Wim Wenders (whose films include *Paris, Texas* and *Wings of Desire*) to direct a video for their version of Cole Porter's 'Night And Day', which they had recorded in Dublin during the summer and would feature on the AIDS awareness LP, *Red Hot + Blue*. They rented a house in East Berlin (which had a plaque outside stating that Leonid Brezhnev had once slept there) and set to work in Hansa's By the Wall Studio—in the same room where several other notable exiles from the English-speaking

rock world had recorded their work, including David Bowie (*Low* and *Heroes*), Iggy Pop, David Byrne and Nick Cave.

The record was being produced by Daniel Lanois and engineered by Flood, the Hansa sound engineer, and although U2 didn't really know what sound they were looking for they knew exactly what they didn't want. Around the time of *The Joshua Tree* there were several possible directions they could have moved in; they had briefly considered a darker, more sombre path on the other side of the 'With Or Without You' single. This was the kind of direction that interested all of them, only this time they would take it much further. It wasn't easy going, however, and it took them a couple of weeks to hit on the right sound and get things under way.

On their return from Berlin they moved into a rented mansion near the coastal village of Dalkey, just south of Dublin, to finish the album,

using a similar kind of set-up to the one that they had employed at Slane Castle in 1984, when they made their last great leap (from *War* to *The Unforgettable Fire*).

Bono feelin' good as "the Fly", on his black acoustic guitar.

"I never knew I was Irish until I went to America"

Bono

During the same period The Edge split up from Aislinn, his partner of the past 11 years, and this was later thought to have influenced the lyrics that Bono was writing for the new LP—*Achtung Baby*.

Achtung Baby

The LP was preceded by a single from it called 'The Fly', released in October 1991, which was basically a very dark dance track that listed a series of truisms in the verses, while the chorus saw man's primal instincts battling with a higher, spiritual side (reflected in a low vocal and a gospel one). The video

showed Bono taking on the character of "the Fly" in the black leather and huge shades which he had first adopted in Berlin.

'The Fly' shot to the top of the UK charts, preparing the way for *Achtung Baby*, which was unlike anything U2 had ever done before. The phrase "Achtung baby" had been repeatedly used by U2's long-serving sound engineer Joe O'Herlihy while the band were in Berlin—a bastardized form of the line "Danke schön, baby" in Mel Brooks' Oscar-winning screenplay *The Producers*. (U2 had considered calling the album *Adam*, which

Right: U2 filming 'The Fly' video in autumn 1991.

Left: The Edge battles it out with "the Fly".

possibly explains why there was a full-frontal nude photograph of the bassist on the cover, even if it was only one of 16 shots!) From the title to the cover to the music inside, U2 blew the myths surrounding them right out the window.

However, the title and the camped-up photos of the band

wearing make-up didn't reflect the seriousness of the music. For once, it was the rhythm section (particularly Larry's killer drum sound) that was at the centre of the sound, particularly on the opening industrial noise terror of 'Zoo Station' (which would be central to U2's live shows) and 'Even Better Than The Real Thing'. Many of the lyrics dealt with sexual obsession, like the chilling 'So Cruel' (which Bono had written as a farewell for Roy Orbison, who had died in December 1988), 'Who's Gonna Ride Your Wild Horses', 'Acrobat' and 'One'. 'Until The End Of The World' dealt with sin and betrayal; this could be interpreted as an act of betrayal on the part of a lover, but Bono later said it was Judas talking to Jesus before he sold him for 30 pieces of silver.

The music for this was also used as the theme for the new Wim Wenders movie of the same name.

The Zoo TV World Tour

Achtung Baby saw U2 dealing with physical and mental violence in a way that they had never done before, and when they embarked

Bono photographs The Edge on stage during the Zoo TV Tour in 1992.

on their Zoo TV World Tour they smashed even more preconceptions. The idea for Zoo TV came from many different sources, one of which was how sensory overload has numbed the world to violence.

This realization hit Bono when he was watching the TV news coverage of the 1990 Gulf War and, horrified by the bombardment of images of human carnage, found himself channel-hopping.

U2's live shows had been pretty straightforward in the past, but the new one reflected the video age and the information overload that has gone with it. The stage set featured four giant video screens and a series of TV monitors which projected a barrage of non-stop images, slogans and an electro/industrial soundtrack. As if that wasn't enough to contend with, the stage spotlights were housed in six brightly coloured Trabant car shells which hung from the lighting rig and shone down on the stage, while an impressive walkway extended from the stage down to the crowd.

Trabant cars shine the spotlight on the Zoo TV stage.

Cultural collision: *Achtung Baby* and a derelict Trabant.

Meanwhile, Bono would assume the character of "the Fly": a black-leathered figure with dark shades, slicked-back hair and a new crotch-grabbing, camera-humping sexual persona thrown into the bargain. During the encore, he would return as "the Mirrorball Man", dressed in a silver lamé suit, carrying a full-length mirror and behaving like the wild-eyed, manic preacher in Flannery O'Connor's *Wiseblood*. The set play list was based on the 12

songs from *Achtung Baby*, opening with 'Zoo Station', a reference to the rail terminus in West Berlin where East Germans coming to the Western part of the city had their first glimpse of the strange, new world of modern capitalist culture—a perfect reflection of Zoo TV.

Calling the President

The tour began in the USA in February 1992 before moving on to Europe and back to the States. Adam suggested that Bono should carry a portable phone, so that he'd be able to call up whomever he might want to speak to during the show. Bono's phone calls proved to be a major highlight, and ranged from President George Bush (who already had an election campaign to deal with) to a dial-a-pizza company with whom the singer placed an order for 100,000

Bono in new persona, as the manic "Mirrorball Man".

The Trabants carried slogans and lyrics as well as lights.

pizzas. In England Bono tried to call Prime Minister John Major, who wasn't home, while in the US Bill Clinton rang into a live radio station to speak to the band because he had heard that they had had trouble getting through to him. Another highlight was 'The Fly' (the song), its message made doubly clear by a stream of mind-zapping graphic slogans on the TV monitors, such as: "Everything You Know Is Wrong", "Rock 'n' Roll Is Entertainment —Over One Billion Served", "Remember What You Dream", plus words like "Napalm", "Sex" and "Death".

According to Bono, the character of "the Fly" was a reaction to the accusations of rampant egotism that followed *Rattle And Hum*—the singer figured that if people already perceived him as an egomaniac then he might as well have some fun being one. As the tour progressed, U2 seemed to be enjoying performing more than ever, varying their set with Bono closing the show with an Elvis

> **"Rock 'n' Roll Is Entertainment —Over One Billion Served"**
>
> *U2*

U2 on *Kenny Live*, an Irish chat show, in Dublin in 1992.

thing that U2 had made an issue of on *Achtung Baby*, printing the address of the Shut Down Sellafield/Windscale Campaign on the sleeve notes so that their fans could voice their complaints too.

number and Larry even getting up to sing the Ewan MacColl classic 'Dirty Old Town'. As far as they were concerned, they had regained the spirit of rock 'n' roll, as well as the sense of humour and mystery that had made them want to form a band in the first place. Bono even appeared on the cover of *Vogue* magazine—the first man for over 25 years.

Political action

But while Zoo TV (and particularly the character of "the Fly") had helped U2 to discard their image as serious statesmen of rock, the band did take one form of direct political action: in June, they decked themselves out in white radiation suits and masks outside the Sellafield nuclear reprocessing plant on the north-west coast of England to protest against the proposed building of a second installation. Sellafield was some-

They also played a Stop Sellafield show at Manchester's G-Mex Centre, alongside Public Enemy and BAD II (and they ended up taking both bands on the second leg of their American tour with them).

This time round U2 were not only attracting their musical heroes to their shows, but also literary greats like Charles Bukowski and William Burroughs. Burroughs even recited a sardonic Thanksgiving Day speech for the band's global TV spectacle, Zoo TV. Directed by ex-10cc drummer Kevin Godley, Zoo TV consisted of live footage and current affairs scratch video and was beamed out to 32 countries in November. For a band that had always striven to smash down barriers, satellite TV was the perfect medium.

The Zooropa Tour

U2 finished the Zoo TV Tour at the end of 1992, but they lined up more European dates for the summer of 1993 (including four shows at London's Wembley Stadium in August). They also aimed to record an EP of new material but, once they started recording, they came up with over a dozen tracks and, to the surprise of their record company, announced that they would release the album in July.

The band take direct action at Sellafield in June 1992.

But first U2 had to begin their Zooropa Tour of Europe. It began in Rotterdam on May 9, and was even more of a hi-tech rock extravaganza than the Zoo Tour. This time the audio-visuals had been worked out between U2 and an American group called EBN (Emergency Broadcast Network). The loop opened with footage of an 11-year-old Nazi boy playing drums at the 1936 Olympic Games. It went on to include many other thought-provoking symbols, sounds and images.

Larry's drums, Adam's bass and The Edge's searing guitar sounded meaner than ever, while Bono unveiled his weirdest character yet: Mister MacPhisto, a cross between Mephistopheles (the devil to whom Faust sold his soul) and Mac-Donalds (suggesting that he is just another product) with an Elvis Presley-style gold lamé suit, a white facepack, a slicked-back ponytail and a scarlet pair of devil's horns. The line in U2's biggest-selling single, 'With Or Without You', about giving away your soul, was ready-made for the eerie MacPhisto.

Bono in devilish mood as Mister MacPhisto.

Zooropa—the album

Yet if MacPhisto seemed eerie, then *Zooropa* was the weirdest, most disturbing album that U2 had ever

Mister MacPhisto makes one of his notorious phone calls during the Zooropa Tour.

Bono prepares to give
his soul away.

made. Produced by Flood, Brian Eno and The Edge, it was recorded in Dublin in 6 weeks between March and May 1993, and confounded those who had expected it to be the mere son of *Achtung Baby*.

Heavily influenced by the work of the cyberpunk novelist William Gibson, *Zooropa* took the listener through the kind of hellish, sci-fi scapes that Gibson describes in his novel *The Sprawl*, and suggests that U2 have fewer answers than ever. Opening with the dreamy 'Zooropa', the ten tracks range from the void of 'Numb' and the dark world of heroin addiction in 'Daddy's Gonna Pay For Your Crashed Car' to the neurotic dance track 'Lemon' and 'Dirty Day' (a song co-written by The Edge and Bono for Charles Bukowski). The record ended on a brilliant note, with Johnny Cash singing 'The Wanderer' under a burnt-out, post-atomic sky.

The biggest band in the world

Off stage, Adam had become engaged to Naomi Campbell, one of the world's most successful models, while U2's new record deal with Island was worth an estimated £130 million ($195 million) for the next six albums. In the history of pop, only Michael Jackson had signed a more lucrative contract. It also made the members of the band and manager Paul McGuinness five of the richest men in Ireland and U2 one of the country's most important industries. Not only had U2's various business ventures created hundreds of jobs but they had also boosted Dublin's tourist trade, since hundreds of tourists were now keen to walk past Windmill Lane (leaving more graffiti than outside EMI's Abbey Road studio during the height of the

The Edge and Bono (as MacPhisto) keep their eyes on the future.

Beatles' fame) and the other places where U2 had taken their first tentative steps in the business.

So although Sting had been right in 1986 when he had handed his guitar to Bono, figuring that U2 were about to become the biggest band in the rock world, he had been wrong when he had said that they too would soon be handing over their instruments to some new "young pretenders". If there are two moments that currently sum up the secret of U2, it's when Mister MacPhisto sings an Elvis Presley ballad while a confusing jumble of visuals flash around him, or when Johnny Cash closes *Zooropa* with 'The Wanderer'. These songs show that U2 have maintained their grasp on the past while not losing sight of the future.

U2 have stayed at the top because they keep changing and keep dreaming—dreaming themselves out of one place right on into another.

CHRONOLOGY

1977

Autumn — U2 play their first show at Dublin's Mount Temple Comprehensive School.

May — U2 find a manager in Paul McGuinness.

1979

September — U2 release their first single, 'U23' (in Ireland only), which reaches Number 1 in the Irish charts.

1980

March — U2 sign to Island Records.

May — U2 release their first British single, '11 O'Clock Tick Tock'.

October — U2 release their first album, *Boy*.

1981

August — U2 have their first UK chart hit with the single 'Fire', which reaches Number 35.

1983

January — U2 have their first UK Top 10 hit with 'New Year's Day'.

March — U2 release their third album, *War*, which reaches Number 1 in the British charts.

June — U2 play at Red Rocks in Denver, California (a show which was later released as the *Under A Blood Red Sky* video, while a couple of the songs from it appeared on the LP of the same name).

1984

July   U2 release their
        first single on their
        own Mother
        Records label (In
        Tua Nua's 'Coming
        Thru').

1985

July   U2 play Live Aid
        on July 13—things
        are never quite the
        same again.

1986

May   U2 play Self-Aid, a
        benefit for
        Ireland's
        unemployed.

June	U2 play alongside Sting, Peter Gabriel, Lou Reed, the Neville Brothers and Bryan Adams on the Conspiracy of Hope International Tour.		**1988**	
		October	The release of U2's *Rattle And Hum* album and movie.	
			1991	
1987		November	U2 release *Achtung Baby*.	
March	U2 release the 14-million-selling *The Joshua Tree*.			

1992

February — U2 begin their Zoo TV World Tour in the United States.

1993

May — U2 begin their Zooropa Tour in Europe.

July — U2 release their new studio album, *Zooropa*.

DISCOGRAPHY

ALBUMS

Boy
October 1980
UK: Island CID 110
US: Island 842296-2
Charts: UK 54, US 94

October
October 1981
UK: Island CID 111
US: Island 842297-2
Charts: UK 11, US 104

War
March 1983
UK: Island CID 112
Charts: UK 1, US 12

The Unforgettable Fire
October 1984
UK: Island U225/CID 25
US: Polygram 822898-2
Charts: UK 1, US 12

The Joshua Tree
March 1987
UK: Island U26/CID 26
US: Island 842298-2
Charts: UK 1, US 1

Rattle And Hum
October 1988
UK: Island U27/CID 27
US: Island 842299-2
Charts: UK 1, US 1

Achtung Baby
November 1991
UK: Island U28/CIDU 28
US: Polygram 510347-2
Charts: UK 1, US 1

Zooropa
July 1993
UK: Island U29/CIDU 29
US: Island 518047-2
Charts: UK 2, US 1

MINI ALBUMS

Under A Blood Red Sky
November 1983
UK: Island CID 113
US: Polygram 818008-2
Charts: UK 1, US 28

Wide Awake In America
October 1987
UK: Island CIDU22
US: (Released May 1985)
Island 90279
Charts: UK 1, US 37

UK SINGLES

U23
(Tracks: Out Of Control; Boy/Girl; Stories For Boys)
September 1979
Charts: Ireland 1

Another Day; Twilight
February 1980
Charts: UK –, US –

11 O'Clock Tick Tock; Touch
May 1980
Charts: UK –, US –

A Day Without Me; Things To Make And Do
August 1980:
Charts: UK –, US –

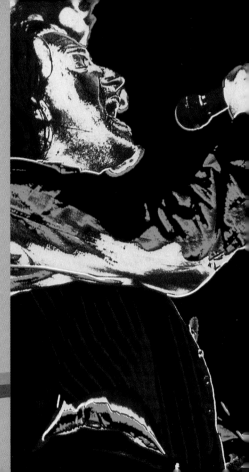

I Will Follow; Boy/Girl
October 1980
Charts: UK –, US –

Fire; J Swallow
July 1981
Charts: UK 35, US –

**Gloria; I Will Follow
(live)**
October 1981
Charts: UK 55, US 81

**A Celebration; Trash,
Trampoline And The
Party Girl**
October 1982
Charts: UK 47, US –

**New Year's Day;
Treasure**
January 1983
Charts: UK 10, US 53

**Two Hearts Beat As
One; Endless Deep**
March 1983
Charts: UK 18, US –

**Pride (In The Name Of
Love); Boomerang**
September 1984
Charts: UK 3, US 33

**The Unforgettable
Fire; A Sort Of
Homecoming (live)**
April 1985
Charts: UK 6, US –

**With Or Without You;
Luminous Times
(Hold On To Love);
Walk To The Water**
March 1987
Charts: UK 4, US 1

I Still Haven't Found
What I'm Looking For;
Spanish Eyes; Deep
In The Heart
May 1987
Charts: UK 6, US 1

Where The Streets
Have No Name; Silver
And Gold; Sweetest
Thing
August 1987
Charts:UK 4, US 13

Desire; Hallelujah
(Here She Comes)
September 1988
Charts: UK 1, US 3

Angel Of Harlem; A
Room At The
Heartbreak Hotel
December 1988
Charts: UK 9, US 14

When Love Comes To
Town; Dancing
Barefoot
April 1989
Charts: UK 6, US 68

All I Want Is You;
Unchained Love
June 1989
Charts: UK 4, US 83

The Fly; Alex
Descends Into Hell
For A Bottle Of Milk:
JKorova 1
October 1991
Charts: UK 1, US 61

Mysterious Ways;
Mysterious Ways
(Solar Plexus Magic
Hour Remix)
December 1991
Charts: UK 13, US 9

One
March 1992
Charts: UK 1, US 10

Even Better Than The
Real Thing
June 1992
UK 12, US 36

Who's Gonna Ride
Your Wild Horses
December 1992
Charts: UK 14, US 35

Numb
August 1993

Under A
Blood Red Sky

The Unforgettable
Fire

Rattle And Hum

Numb

INDEX

All page numbers in *italics* refer to illustrations

Index

Picture acknowledgements

Photographs reproduced by kind permission of London Features International; Pictorial Press/G. Chin, /Terry McGough, /John Mayer, /V. Zuffante; Redferns/Mike Cameron, /Peter Cronin, /Erica Echenberg, /Bob King, /Ebet Roberts; Retna/Mark Anderson, /Jay Blakesberg, /Adrian Boot, /David Corrio, /Kevin Cummins, /Steve Double, /Tim Jarvis, /Patrick Quigley, /Rikken, /Lex Van Rossen, /Paul Slattery, /Ann Summa; S.I.N./David Corrio.

Front cover picture: London Features International.